MATLAB®

STUDENT VERSION

The MATH WORKS Inc.

Learning MATLAB

Version 5.3 (Release 11)

How to Contact The MathWorks:

www.mathworks.com	Web
ftp.mathworks.com	Anonymous FTP server
comp.soft-sys.matlab	Newsgroup

@

support@mathworks.com	Technical support
suggest@mathworks.com	Product enhancement suggestions
bugs@mathworks.com	Bug reports
doc@mathworks.com	Documentation error reports
subscribe@mathworks.com	Subscribing user registration
service@mathworks.com	Order status, license renewals, passcodes
info@mathworks.com	Sales, pricing, and general information

☎ 508-647-7000 Phone

508-647-7001 Fax

✉ The MathWorks, Inc. Mail
3 Apple Hill Drive
Natick, MA 01760-2098

ISBN 0-9672195-1-5

Printing History: August 1999   First printing   New manual

Contents

Introduction

1

Installation

2

Getting Started

3

Graphics

4

Programming with MATLAB

5

Symbolic Math Toolbox

6

MATLAB Quick Reference

A

Symbolic Math Toolbox Quick Reference

B

1

Introduction

About the Student Version

The Student Version of MATLAB® & Simulink® is the premier software package for technical computation, data analysis, and visualization in education and industry. The Student Version of MATLAB & Simulink provides all of the features of professional MATLAB, with no limitations, and the full functionality of professional Simulink, with model sizes up to 300 blocks. The Student Version gives you immediate access to the high-performance numeric computing power you need.

MATLAB allows you to focus on your course work and applications rather than on programming details. It enables you to solve many numerical problems in a fraction of the time it would take you to write a program in a lower level language. MATLAB helps you better understand and apply concepts in applications ranging from engineering and mathematics to chemistry, biology, and economics.

Simulink, included with the Student Version, provides a block diagram tool for modeling and simulating dynamical systems, including signal processing, controls, communications, and other complex systems.

The Symbolic Math Toolbox, also included with the Student Version, is based on the Maple®V symbolic kernel and lets you perform symbolic computations and variable-precision arithmetic.

MATLAB products are used in a broad range of industries, including automotive, aerospace, electronics, environmental, telecommunications, computer peripherals, finance, and medical. More than 400,000 technical professionals at the world's most innovative technology companies, government research labs, financial institutions, and at more than 2,000 universities rely on MATLAB and Simulink as the fundamental tools for their engineering and scientific work.

Student Use Policy

This Student License is for use in conjunction with courses offered at a degree-granting institution. The MathWorks offers this license as a special service to the student community and asks your help in seeing that its terms are not abused.

To use this Student License, you must be a student using the software in conjunction with courses offered at degree-granting institutions.

You may not use this Student License at a company or government lab, or if you are an instructor at a university. Also, you may not use it for research or for commercial or industrial purposes. In these cases, you can acquire the appropriate professional or academic version of the software by contacting The MathWorks.

Differences Between the Student Version and the Professional Version

MATLAB

This version of MATLAB provides full support for all language features as well as graphics, external (Application Program Interface) support, and access to every other feature of the professional version of MATLAB.

Note MATLAB does not have a matrix size limitation in this Student Version.

MATLAB Differences. There are a few small differences between the Student Version and the professional version of MATLAB:

1 The MATLAB prompt in the Student Version is

```
EDU>>
```

2 The window title bars include the words

```
<Student Version>
```

3 All printouts contain the footer

```
Student Version of MATLAB
```

This footer is not an option that can be turned off; it will always appear in your printouts.

Simulink

This Student Version contains the complete Simulink product, which is used with MATLAB to model, simulate, and analyze dynamical systems.

Simulink Differences.

1 Models are limited to 300 blocks.

2 The window title bars include the words

   `<Student Version>`

3 All printouts contain the footer

   `Student Version of MATLAB`

   This footer is not an option that can be turned off; it will always appear in your printouts.

Obtaining Additional MathWorks Products

Many college courses recommend MATLAB as their standard instructional software. In some cases, the courses may require particular toolboxes, blocksets, or other products. Many of these products are available for student use. You may purchase and download these additional products at special student prices from the MathWorks Store at www.mathworks.com/store.

Although many professional toolboxes are available at student prices from the MathWorks Store, *not* every one is available for student use. Some of the toolboxes you can purchase include:

Communications	Neural Network
Control System	Optimization
Fuzzy Logic	Signal Processing
Image Processing	Statistics

For an up-to-date list of which toolboxes are available, visit the MathWorks Store.

Note The toolboxes that are available for the Student Version of MATLAB & Simulink have the same functionality as the full, professional versions. However, these student versions will *only* work with the Student Version. Likewise, the professional versions of the toolboxes will *not* work with the Student Version.

Patches and Updates

From time to time, the MathWorks makes changes to some of its products between scheduled releases. When this happens, these updates are made available from our Web site. As a registered user of the Student Version, you will be notified by e-mail of the availability of product updates.

Note To register your product, see "Product Registration" in "Troubleshooting and Other Resources" in this chapter.

Getting Started with MATLAB

What I Want	What I Should Do
I need to install MATLAB.	See Chapter 2, "Installation," in this book.
I'm new to MATLAB and want to learn it quickly.	Start by reading Chapters 1 through 5 of *Learning MATLAB*. The most important things to learn are how to enter matrices, how to use the : (colon) operator, and how to invoke functions. You will also get a brief overview of graphics and programming in MATLAB. After you master the basics, you can access the rest of the documentation through the online help (Help Desk) facility.
I want to look at some samples of what you can do with MATLAB.	There are numerous demonstrations included with MATLAB. You can see the demos by selecting **Examples and Demos** from the **Help** menu. (Linux users type demo at the MATLAB prompt.) There are demos in mathematics, graphics, visualization, and much more. You also will find a large selection of demos at www.mathworks.com/demos.

Finding Reference Information

What I Want	What I Should Do
I want to know how to use a specific function.	Use the online help (Help Desk) facility, or, use the M-file help window to get brief online help. These are available using the command helpdesk or from the **Help** menu on the PC. The MATLAB Function Reference is also available on the Help Desk in PDF format (under **Online Manuals**) if you want to print out any of the function descriptions in high-quality form.
I want to find a function for a specific purpose but I don't know its name.	There are several choices: • Use lookfor (e.g., lookfor inverse) from the command line. • See Appendix A, "MATLAB Quick Reference," in this book for a list of MATLAB functions. • From the Help Desk peruse the MATLAB functions by Subject or by Index. • Use the full text search from the Help Desk.
I want to learn about a specific topic like sparse matrices, ordinary differential equations, or cell arrays.	Use the Help Desk facility to locate the appropriate chapter in *Using MATLAB*.
I want to know what functions are available in a general area.	Use the Help Desk facility to see the Function Reference grouped by subject, or see Appendix A, "MATLAB Quick Reference," in this book for a list of MATLAB functions. The Help Desk provides access to the reference pages for the hundreds of functions included with MATLAB.
I want to learn about the Symbolic Math Toolbox.	See Chapter 6, "Symbolic Math Toolbox," and Appendix B, "Symbolic Math Toolbox Quick Reference," in this book. For complete descriptions of the Symbolic Math Toolbox functions, use the Help Desk and select Symbolic Math Toolbox functions.

Troubleshooting and Other Resources

What I Want	What I Should Do
I have a MATLAB specific problem I want help with.	Visit the Technical Support section (www.mathworks.com/support) of the MathWorks Web site and use the Solution Support Engine to search the Knowledge Base of problem solutions.
I want to report a bug or make a suggestion.	Use the Help Desk or send e-mail to bugs@mathworks.com or suggest@mathworks.com.

Documentation Library

Your Student Version of MATLAB & Simulink contains much more documentation than the two printed books, *Learning MATLAB* and *Learning Simulink*. On your CD is a personal reference library of every book and reference page distributed by The MathWorks. Access this documentation library from the Help Desk.

Note Even though you have the documentation set for the MathWorks family of products, not every product is available for the Student Version of MATLAB & Simulink. For an up-to-date list of available products, visit the MathWorks Store. At the store you can also purchase printed manuals for the MATLAB family of products.

Accessing the Online Documentation

Access the online documentation (Help Desk) directly from your product CD. (Linux users should refer to Chapter 2, "Installation," for specific information on configuring and accessing the Help Desk from the CD.)

1 Place the CD in your CD-ROM drive.

2 Select **Documentation (Help Desk)** from the **Help** menu.

The Help Desk appears in a Web browser.

Usenet Newsgroup

If you have access to Usenet newsgroups, you can join the active community of participants in the MATLAB specific group, `comp.soft-sys.matlab`. This forum is a gathering of professionals and students who use MATLAB and have questions or comments about it and its associated products. This is a great resource for posing questions and answering those of others. MathWorks staff also participates actively in this newsgroup.

MathWorks Web Site

Use your browser to visit the MathWorks Web site, `www.mathworks.com`. You'll find lots of information about MathWorks products and how they are used in education and industry, product demos, and MATLAB based books. From the Web site you will also be able to access our technical support resources, view a library of user and company supplied M-files, and get information about products and upcoming events.

MathWorks Education Web Site

This education-specific Web site, `www.mathworks.com/education`, contains many resources for various branches of mathematics and science. Many of these include teaching examples, books, and other related products. You will also find a comprehensive list of links to Web sites where MATLAB is used for teaching and research at universities.

MATLAB Related Books

Hundreds of MATLAB related books are available from many different publishers. An up-to-date list is available at `www.mathworks.com/books`.

MathWorks Store

The MathWorks Store (`www.mathworks.com/store`) gives you an easy way to purchase products, upgrades, and documentation.

MathWorks Knowledge Base

You can access the MathWorks Knowledge Base from the Support link on our Web site. Our Technical Support group maintains this database of frequently asked questions (FAQ). You can peruse the Knowledge Base by topics, categories, or use the Solution Search Engine to quickly locate relevant data. You can answer many of your questions by spending a few minutes with this around-the-clock resource.

Also, Technical Notes, which is accessible from our Technical Support Web site (www.mathworks.com/support), contains numerous examples on graphics, mathematics, API, Simulink, and others.

Technical Support

Registered users of the Student Version of MATLAB & Simulink can use our electronic technical support services to answer product questions. Visit our Technical Support Web site at www.mathworks.com/support.

Student Version Support Policy

The MathWorks does not provide telephone technical support to users of the Student Version of MATLAB & Simulink. There are numerous other vehicles of technical support that you can use. The Sources of Information card included with the Student Version identifies the ways to obtain support.

After checking the available MathWorks sources for help, if you still cannot resolve your problem, you should contact your instructor. Your instructor should be able to help you, but if not, there is telephone technical support for registered instructors who have adopted the Student Version of MATLAB & Simulink in their courses.

Product Registration

Visit the MathWorks Web site (www.mathworks.com/student) and register your Student Version.

About MATLAB and Simulink

What Is MATLAB?

MATLAB is a high-performance language for technical computing. It integrates computation, visualization, and programming in an easy-to-use environment where problems and solutions are expressed in familiar mathematical notation. Typical uses include:

- Math and computation
- Algorithm development
- Modeling, simulation, and prototyping
- Data analysis, exploration, and visualization
- Scientific and engineering graphics
- Application development, including graphical user interface building

MATLAB is an interactive system whose basic data element is an array that does not require dimensioning. This allows you to solve many technical computing problems, especially those with matrix and vector formulations, in a fraction of the time it would take to write a program in a scalar noninteractive language such as C or Fortran.

The name MATLAB stands for *matrix laboratory*. MATLAB was originally written to provide easy access to matrix software developed by the LINPACK and EISPACK projects, which together represent the state-of-the-art in software for matrix computation.

MATLAB has evolved over a period of years with input from many users. In university environments, it is the standard instructional tool for introductory and advanced courses in mathematics, engineering, and science. In industry, MATLAB is the tool of choice for high-productivity research, development, and analysis.

Toolboxes

MATLAB features a family of application-specific solutions called *toolboxes*. Very important to most users of MATLAB, toolboxes allow you to *learn* and *apply* specialized technology. Toolboxes are comprehensive collections of MATLAB functions (M-files) that extend the MATLAB environment to solve particular classes of problems. Areas in which toolboxes are available include signal processing, control systems, neural networks, fuzzy logic, wavelets, simulation, and many others.

The MATLAB System

The MATLAB system consists of five main parts:

The MATLAB language.   This is a high-level matrix/array language with control flow statements, functions, data structures, input/output, and object-oriented programming features. It allows both "programming in the small" to rapidly create quick and dirty throw-away programs, and "programming in the large" to create complete large and complex application programs.

The MATLAB working environment.   This is the set of tools and facilities that you work with as the MATLAB user or programmer. It includes facilities for managing the variables in your workspace and importing and exporting data. It also includes tools for developing, managing, debugging, and profiling M-files, MATLAB's applications.

Handle Graphics®.   This is the MATLAB graphics system. It includes high-level commands for two-dimensional and three-dimensional data visualization, image processing, animation, and presentation graphics. It also includes low-level commands that allow you to fully customize the appearance of graphics as well as to build complete graphical user interfaces on your MATLAB applications.

The MATLAB mathematical function library.   This is a vast collection of computational algorithms ranging from elementary functions like sum, sine, cosine, and complex arithmetic, to more sophisticated functions like matrix inverse, matrix eigenvalues, Bessel functions, and fast Fourier transforms.

The MATLAB Application Program Interface (API).   This is a library that allows you to write C and Fortran programs that interact with MATLAB. It include facilities for calling routines from MATLAB (dynamic linking), calling MATLAB as a computational engine, and for reading and writing MAT-files.

What Is Simulink?

Simulink, a companion program to MATLAB, is an interactive system for simulating nonlinear dynamic systems. It is a graphical mouse-driven program that allows you to model a system by drawing a block diagram on the screen and manipulating it dynamically. It can work with linear, nonlinear, continuous-time, discrete-time, multirate, and hybrid systems.

Blocksets are add-ons to Simulink that provide additional libraries of blocks for specialized applications like communications, signal processing, and power systems.

Real-Time Workshop® is a program that allows you to generate C code from your block diagrams and to run it on a variety of real-time systems.

The MATLAB Product Family

This figure shows how the MathWorks products fit together.

MATLAB is the foundation for all the MathWorks products. MATLAB combines numeric computation, 2-D and 3-D graphics, and language capabilities in a single, easy-to-use environment.

MATLAB Extensions are optional tools that support the implementation of systems developed in MATLAB.

Toolboxes are libraries of MATLAB functions that customize MATLAB for solving particular classes of problems. Toolboxes are open and extensible; you can view algorithms and add your own.

Simulink is a system for nonlinear simulation that combines a block diagram interface and "live" simulation capabilities with the core numeric, graphics, and language functionality of MATLAB.

Simulink Extensions are optional tools that support the implementation of systems developed in Simulink

Blocksets are collections of Simulink blocks designed for use in specific application areas.

MATLAB

Simulink

MATLAB Extensions

- MATLAB Compiler
- MATLAB C/C ++ Math Libraries
- MATLAB Web Server
- MATLAB Report Generator

Toolboxes

- Control System
- Communications
- Database
- Financial
- Frequency Domain System Identification
- Fuzzy Logic
- Higher Order Spectral Analysis
- Image Processing
- LMI Control
- Model Predictive Control
- μ–Analysis and Synthesis
- Neural Network
- Optimization
- Partial Differential Equation
- Robust Control
- Signal Processing
- Spline
- Statistics
- Symbolic Math
- System Identification
- Wavelet

Simulink Extensions

- Simulink Accelerator
- Real-Time Workshop
- Real-Time Windows Target
- Stateflow®

Blocksets

- DSP
- Fixed-Point
- Nonlinear Control Design
- Power System

Contact The MathWorks or visit www.mathworks.com for an up-to-date product list.

2

Installation

Installing on a PC

System Requirements

Note For the most up-to-date information about system requirements, see the system requirements page, available in the Products area at the MathWorks Web site (www.mathworks.com).

MATLAB and Simulink

- Intel-based Pentium, Pentium Pro, or Pentium II personal computer
- Microsoft Windows 95, Windows 98, or Windows NT 4.0 (with Service Pack 3)
- CD-ROM drive (for installation and online documentation)
- 16 MB RAM minimum for Windows 95 and 98; 16 MB RAM minimum for Windows NT, 24 MB (or more) strongly recommended
- Disk space varies depending on size of partition. The MATLAB installer will inform you of the hard disk space requirement for your particular partition. For example:
  - Partition with a 512-byte cluster size requires 53 MB for MATLAB and Simulink
  - Partition with a 64K-byte cluster size requires 223 MB for MATLAB and Simulink
- 8-bit graphics adapter and display (for 256 simultaneous colors)

Other recommended items include:

- Microsoft Windows supported graphics accelerator card
- Microsoft Windows supported printer
- Microsoft Windows supported sound card
- Netscape Navigator 3.0 or higher or Microsoft Internet Explorer 4.0 (to view the online documentation)
- Microsoft Word 7.0 (Office 95), or 8.0 (Office 97) (to run the MATLAB Notebook)

Adobe Acrobat Reader is required to view and print the MATLAB online documentation that is in PDF format. Adobe Acrobat Reader is available on the MATLAB CD.

MEX-Files

MEX-files are dynamically linked subroutines that MATLAB can automatically load and execute. They provide a mechanism by which you can call your own C and Fortran subroutines from MATLAB as if they were built-in functions.

For More Information The *Application Program Interface Guide* describes how to write MEX-files and the *Application Program Interface Reference* describes the collection of API functions. Both of these are available from the Help Desk.

If you plan to build your own MEX-files, one of the following is required:

- DEC Visual Fortran version 5.0 or 6.0
- Microsoft Visual C/C++ version 4.2, 5.0, or 6.0
- Borland C++ version 5.0, 5.2, or 5.3
- Watcom C/C++ version 10.6 or 11

Note For an up-to-date list of all the compilers supported by MATLAB, see the MathWorks Technical Support Department's Technical Notes at www.mathworks.com/support/tech-notes/#mex.

Installing MATLAB

This list summarizes the steps in the standard installation procedure. You can perform the installation by simply following the instructions in the dialog boxes presented by the installation program; it walks you through this process.

1 Stop any virus protection software you have running.

2 Insert the MathWorks CD into your CD-ROM drive. The installation program starts automatically when the CD-ROM drive is ready. You can also run setup.exe from the CD. View the **Welcome** screen.

3 Review the Student Use Policy.

4 Review the Software License Agreement.

5 Enter your name and school name.

6 To install the complete set of software (MATLAB, Simulink, and the Symbolic Math Toolbox), make sure all of the components are selected in the **Select MATLAB Components** dialog box.

7 Specify the destination directory, that is, the directory where you want to save the files on your hard drive. To change directories, use the **Browse** button.

8 When the installation is complete, verify the installation by starting MATLAB and running one of the demo programs.

9 Customize any MATLAB environment options, if desired. For example, to include default definitions or any MATLAB expressions that you want executed every time MATLAB is invoked, create a file named startup.m in the $MATLAB\toolbox\local directory. MATLAB executes this file each time MATLAB is invoked.

10 Perform any additional necessary configuration by typing the appropriate command at the MATLAB command prompt. For example, to configure the MATLAB Notebook, type notebook -setup. To configure a compiler to work with the MATLAB Application Program Interface, type mex -setup.

For More Information The *MATLAB Installation Guide for PC* provides additional installation information. This manual is available in PDF form from **Online Manuals** on the Help Desk.

Installing Additional Toolboxes

To purchase additional toolboxes, visit the MathWorks Store at (www.mathworks.com/store). Once you purchase a toolbox, it is downloaded to your computer.

When you download a toolbox, you receive an installation program for the toolbox. To install the toolbox, run the installation program by double-clicking on its icon. After you successfully install the toolbox, all of its functionality will be available to you when you start MATLAB.

Note Some toolboxes have ReadMe files associated with them. When you download the toolbox, check to see if there is a ReadMe file. These files contain important information about the toolbox and possibly installation and configuration notes. To view the ReadMe file for a toolbox, use the whatsnew command.

Accessing the Online Documentation (Help Desk)

Access the online documentation (Help Desk) directly from your product CD:

1 Place the CD in your CD-ROM drive.

2 Select **Documentation (Help Desk)** from the **Help** menu in the MATLAB command window. You can also type helpdesk at the MATLAB prompt.

The Help Desk, similar to this figure, appears in your Web browser.

MATLAB Help Desk

MATLAB Topics

- MATLAB Functions
  By Subject
  By Index
  Quick Reference in PDF
  Format
- Learning MATLAB
- Using MATLAB
- Using MATLAB Graphics
- Handle Graphics Properties
- MATLAB Environment
- Application Program Interface
  Guide
- Application Program Interface
  Reference
- Known Software and
  Documentation Problems

Go to MATLAB function: [   ] Go

Full-text Search

Online Manuals (in PDF)

Simulink Topics

- Using Simulink
- Writing S-Functions

Symbolic Math Toolbox

- Symbolic Math Toolbox
  Functions

Other Topics

- Toolboxes and Blockset
- Additional Products

The MathWorks Web Site
(Internet Access Required)

- Solution Search
- Questions, Suggestions, and
  Bug Report Forms

www.mathworks.com

Give Us Your Feedback

Installing on Linux

System Requirements

Note For the most up-to-date information about system requirements, see the system requirements page, available in the products area at the MathWorks Web site (www.mathworks.com).

MATLAB and Simulink

- Intel-based Pentium, Pentium Pro, or Pentium II personal computer
- Linux 2.0.34 kernel (Red Hat 4.2, 5.1, Debian 2.0)
- X Windows (X11R6)
- 60 MB free disk space for MATLAB & Simulink
- 64 MB memory, additional memory strongly recommended
- 64 MB swap space (recommended)
- CD-ROM drive (for installation and online documentation)
- 8-bit graphics adapter and display (for 256 simultaneous colors)
- Netscape Navigator 3.0 or higher (to view the online documentation)

Adobe Acrobat Reader is required to view and print the MATLAB online documentation that is in PDF format. Adobe Acrobat Reader is available on the MATLAB CD.

MEX-Files

MEX-files are dynamically linked subroutines that MATLAB can automatically load and execute. They provide a mechanism by which you can call your own C and Fortran subroutines from MATLAB as if they were built-in functions.

For More Information The *Application Program Interface Guide* describes how to write MEX-files and the *Application Program Interface Reference* describes the collection of API functions. Both of these are available from the Help Desk.

If you plan to build your own MEX-files, you need an ANSIC C compiler (e.g., the GNU C compiler, gcc).

Note For an up-to-date list of all the compilers supported by MATLAB, see the MathWorks Technical Support Department's Technical Notes at www.mathworks.com/support/tech-notes/#mex.

Installing MATLAB

The following instructions describe how to install the Student Version of MATLAB & Simulink on your computer.

Note It is recommended that you log in as root to perform your installation.

Installing the Software

To install the Student Version:

1 If your CD-ROM drive is not accessible to your operating system, you will need to create a directory to be the mount point for it.

   ```
   mkdir /cdrom
   ```

2 Place the CD into the CD-ROM drive.

3 Execute the command to mount the CD-ROM drive on your system. For example,

```
# mount -t iso9660 /dev/cdrom /cdrom
```

should work on most systems. If your /etc/fstab file has a line similar to

```
/dev/cdrom /cdrom iso9660 noauto,ro,user,exec 0 0
```

then nonroot users can mount the CD-ROM using the simplified command

```
$ mount /cdrom
```

Note If the exec option is missing (as it often is by default, for security reasons), you will receive a "Permission denied" error when attempting to run the install script. To remedy this, either use the full mount command shown above (as root) or add the exec option to the file /etc/fstab.

---

4 Move to the installation location using the cd command. For example, if you are going to install into the location /usr/local/matlab5, use the commands

```
cd /usr/local
mkdir matlab5
cd matlab5
```

Subsequent instructions in this section refer to this directory as $MATLAB.

5 Copy the license file, license.dat, from the CD to $MATLAB.

6 Run the CD install script.

```
/cdrom/install_lnx86.sh
```

The welcome screen appears. Select **OK** to proceed with the installation.

Note If you need additional help on any step during this installation process, click the **Help** button at the bottom of the dialog box.

---

7 Accept or reject the software licensing agreement displayed. If you accept the terms of the agreement, you may proceed with the installation.

8 The **MATLAB Root Directory** screen is displayed. Select **OK** if the pathname for the MATLAB root directory is correct; otherwise, change it to the desired location.

```
┌─────────────────────────────────────────────────────┐
│                 MATLAB Root Directory                 │
├─────────────────────────────────────────────────────┤
│                                                       │
│   MATLAB root directory location:                     │
│                                                       │
│   │ /usr/local/matlab5                             │  │
│                                                       │
├─────────────────────────────────────────────────────┤
│   ┌──────────┐     ┌──────────┐      ┌──────────┐    │
│   │    OK    │     │  Cancel  │      │   Help   │    │
│   └──────────┘     └──────────┘      └──────────┘    │
└─────────────────────────────────────────────────────┘
```

9 The system displays your license file. Press **OK**.

10 The installation program displays the **Product Installation Options** screen, which is similar to this.

The products you are licensed to install are listed in the **Items to install** list box. The right list box displays the products that you do not want to install. To install the complete Student Version of MATLAB & Simulink, you must install all the products for which you are licensed (MATLAB, MATLAB Toolbox, MATLAB Kernel, Simulink, Symbolic Math, Symbolic Math Library, and GhostScript). Select **OK**.

11 The installation program displays the **Installation Data** screen.

Specify the directory location in your file system for symbolic links to the matlab, matlabdoc, and mex scripts. Choose a directory such as /usr/local/bin. You must be logged in as root to do this.

In the MATLAB License No. field, enter student.

Select **OK** to continue.

12 The **Begin Installation** screen is displayed. Select **OK** to start the installation. After the installation is complete, the **Installation Complete** screen is displayed, assuming your installation is successful. Select **Exit** to exit from the setup program.

13 If desired, customize any MATLAB environment options. For example, to include default definitions or any MATLAB expressions that you want executed every time MATLAB is invoked, create a file named startup.m in the $MATLAB/toolbox/local directory. MATLAB executes this file each time MATLAB is invoked.

14 You must edit the docopt.m M-file located in the $MATLAB/toolbox/local directory to specify the path to the online documentation (Help Desk). For example, if /cdrom is the path to your CD-ROM drive, then you would use

/cdrom/help. To set the path using this example, change the lines in the
if isunix block in the docopt.m file to

```
if isunix                   % UNIX
%    doccmd = '';
%    options = '';
     docpath = '/cdrom/help';
```

The docopt.m file also allows you to specify an alternative Web browser or
additional initial browser options. It is configured for Netscape Navigator.

15 Start MATLAB by entering the matlab command. If you did not set up
symbolic links in a directory on your path, type $MATLAB/bin/matlab.

Post Installation Procedures

Successful Installation

If you want to use the MATLAB Application Program Interface, you must
configure the mex script to work with your compiler. Also, some toolboxes may
require some additional configuration. For more information, see "Installing
Additional Toolboxes" later in this section.

Unsuccessful Installation

If MATLAB does not execute correctly after installation:

1 Check the *MATLAB Known Software and Documentation Problems*
document for the latest information concerning installation. This document
is accessible from the Help Desk.

2 Repeat the installation procedure from the beginning but run the CD install
script using the -t option.

```
/cdrom/install_lnx86.sh -t
```

For More Information The *MATLAB Installation Guide for UNIX* provides
additional installation information. This manual is available in PDF form
from **Online Manuals** on the Help Desk.

2-13

Installing Additional Toolboxes

To purchase additional toolboxes, visit the MathWorks Store at (www.mathworks.com/store). Once you purchase a toolbox, it is downloaded to your computer. When you download a toolbox on Linux, you receive a tar file (a standard, compressed formatted file).

To install the toolbox, you must:

1 Place the tar file in $MATLAB and un-tar it.

```
tar -xf filename
```

2 Run install_matlab.

After you successfully install the toolbox, all of its functionality will be available to you when you start MATLAB.

Note Some toolboxes have ReadMe files associated with them. When you download the toolbox, check to see if there is a ReadMe file. These files contain important information about the toolbox and possibly installation and configuration notes. To view the ReadMe file for a toolbox, use the whatsnew command.

Accessing the Online Documentation (Help Desk)

Access the online documentation (Help Desk) directly from your product CD:

1 Place the CD in your CD-ROM drive and mount it.

2 Type helpdesk at the MATLAB prompt.

The Help Desk, similar to this figure, appears in your Web browser.

3

Getting Started

Starting MATLAB

This book is intended to help you start learning MATLAB. It contains a number of examples, so you should run MATLAB and follow along.

To run MATLAB on a PC, double-click on the MATLAB icon. To run MATLAB on a Linux system, type `matlab` at the operating system prompt. To quit MATLAB at any time, type `quit` at the MATLAB prompt.

If you feel you need more assistance, you can:

- Access the Help Desk by typing `helpdesk` at the MATLAB prompt.
- Type `help` at the MATLAB prompt.
- Pull down the **Help** menu on a PC.

For more information about help and online documentation, see "Help and Online Documentation" later in this chapter. Also, Chapter 1 provides additional help resources.

Matrices and Magic Squares

The best way for you to get started with MATLAB is to learn how to handle matrices. This section shows you how to do that. In MATLAB, a matrix is a rectangular array of numbers. Special meaning is sometimes attached to 1-by-1 matrices, which are scalars, and to matrices with only one row or column, which are vectors. MATLAB has other ways of storing both numeric and nonnumeric data, but in the beginning, it is usually best to think of everything as a matrix. The operations in MATLAB are designed to be as natural as possible. Where other programming languages work with numbers one at a time, MATLAB allows you to work with entire matrices quickly and easily.

A good example matrix, used throughout this book, appears in the Renaissance engraving Melancholia I by the German artist and amateur mathematician Albrecht Dürer. This image is filled with mathematical symbolism, and if you look carefully, you will see a matrix in the upper right corner. This matrix is known as a magic square and was believed by many in Dürer's time to have genuinely magical properties. It does turn out to have some fascinating characteristics worth exploring.

Entering Matrices

You can enter matrices into MATLAB in several different ways:

- Enter an explicit list of elements.
- Load matrices from external data files.
- Generate matrices using built-in functions.
- Create matrices with your own functions in M-files.

Start by entering Dürer's matrix as a list of its elements. You have only to follow a few basic conventions:

- Separate the elements of a row with blanks or commas.
- Use a semicolon, ; , to indicate the end of each row.
- Surround the entire list of elements with square brackets, [ ].

To enter Dürer's matrix, simply type

```
A = [16 3 2 13; 5 10 11 8; 9 6 7 12; 4 15 14 1]
```

MATLAB displays the matrix you just entered,

```
A =
    16     3     2    13
     5    10    11     8
     9     6     7    12
     4    15    14     1
```

This exactly matches the numbers in the engraving. Once you have entered the matrix, it is automatically remembered in the MATLAB workspace. You can refer to it simply as A. Now that you have A in the workspace, take a look at what makes it so interesting. Why is it magic?

sum, transpose, and diag

You're probably already aware that the special properties of a magic square have to do with the various ways of summing its elements. If you take the sum along any row or column, or along either of the two main diagonals, you will always get the same number. Let's verify that using MATLAB. The first statement to try is

```
sum(A)
```

MATLAB replies with

```
ans =
    34    34    34    34
```

When you don't specify an output variable, MATLAB uses the variable ans, short for *answer*, to store the results of a calculation. You have computed a row vector containing the sums of the columns of A. Sure enough, each of the columns has the same sum, the *magic* sum, 34.

How about the row sums? MATLAB has a preference for working with the columns of a matrix, so the easiest way to get the row sums is to transpose the matrix, compute the column sums of the transpose, and then transpose the result. The transpose operation is denoted by an apostrophe or single quote, '. It flips a matrix about its main diagonal and it turns a row vector into a column vector. So

```
A'
```

produces

```
ans =
      16        5        9        4
       3       10        6       15
       2       11        7       14
      13        8       12        1
```

And

```
sum(A')'
```

produces a column vector containing the row sums

```
ans =
      34
      34
      34
      34
```

The sum of the elements on the main diagonal is easily obtained with the help of the diag function, which picks off that diagonal.

```
diag(A)
```

produces

```
ans =
      16
      10
       7
       1
```

and

```
sum(diag(A))
```

produces

```
ans =
      34
```

The other diagonal, the so-called *antidiagonal,* is not so important mathematically, so MATLAB does not have a ready-made function for it. But a function originally intended for use in graphics, fliplr, flips a matrix from left to right.

```
sum(diag(fliplr(A)))

ans =
    34
```

You have verified that the matrix in Dürer's engraving is indeed a magic square and, in the process, have sampled a few MATLAB matrix operations. The following sections continue to use this matrix to illustrate additional MATLAB capabilities.

Subscripts

The element in row i and column j of A is denoted by A(i,j). For example, A(4,2) is the number in the fourth row and second column. For our magic square, A(4,2) is 15. So it is possible to compute the sum of the elements in the fourth column of A by typing

```
A(1,4) + A(2,4) + A(3,4) + A(4,4)
```

This produces

```
ans =
    34
```

but is not the most elegant way of summing a single column.

It is also possible to refer to the elements of a matrix with a single subscript, A(k). This is the usual way of referencing row and column vectors. But it can also apply to a fully two-dimensional matrix, in which case the array is regarded as one long column vector formed from the columns of the original matrix. So, for our magic square, A(8) is another way of referring to the value 15 stored in A(4,2).

If you try to use the value of an element outside of the matrix, it is an error.

```
t = A(4,5)
Index exceeds matrix dimensions.
```

On the other hand, if you store a value in an element outside of the matrix, the size increases to accommodate the newcomer.

```
X = A;
X(4,5) = 17

X =
    16     3     2    13     0
     5    10    11     8     0
     9     6     7    12     0
     4    15    14     1    17
```

The Colon Operator

The colon, :, is one of MATLAB's most important operators. It occurs in several different forms. The expression

```
1:10
```

is a row vector containing the integers from 1 to 10

```
 1    2    3    4    5    6    7    8    9    10
```

To obtain nonunit spacing, specify an increment. For example,

```
100:-7:50
```

is

```
100    93    86    79    72    65    58    51
```

and

```
0:pi/4:pi
```

is

```
 0    0.7854    1.5708    2.3562    3.1416
```

Subscript expressions involving colons refer to portions of a matrix.

```
A(1:k,j)
```

is the first k elements of the jth column of A. So

```
sum(A(1:4,4))
```

computes the sum of the fourth column. But there is a better way. The colon by itself refers to *all* the elements in a row or column of a matrix and the keyword end refers to the *last* row or column. So

```
sum(A(:,end))
```

computes the sum of the elements in the last column of A.

```
ans =
    34
```

Why is the magic sum for a 4-by-4 square equal to 34? If the integers from 1 to 16 are sorted into four groups with equal sums, that sum must be

```
sum(1:16)/4
```

which, of course, is

```
ans =
    34
```

The magic Function

Using the Symbolic Math Toolbox, you can discover that the magic sum for an n-by-n magic square is $(n^3 + n)/2$.

MATLAB actually has a built-in function that creates magic squares of almost any size. Not surprisingly, this function is named magic.

```
B = magic(4)

B =
    16     2     3    13
     5    11    10     8
     9     7     6    12
     4    14    15     1
```

This matrix is almost the same as the one in the Dürer engraving and has all the same "magic" properties; the only difference is that the two middle columns are exchanged. To make this B into Dürer's A, swap the two middle columns.

```
A = B(:,[1 3 2 4])
```

This says "for each of the rows of matrix B, reorder the elements in the order 1, 3, 2, 4." It produces

```
A =
    16     3     2    13
     5    10    11     8
     9     6     7    12
     4    15    14     1
```

Why would Dürer go to the trouble of rearranging the columns when he could have used MATLAB's ordering? No doubt he wanted to include the date of the engraving, 1514, at the bottom of his magic square.

For More Information *Using MATLAB* provides comprehensive material on the MATLAB language, environment, mathematical topics, and programming in MATLAB. Access *Using MATLAB* from the Help Desk.

Expressions

Like most other programming languages, MATLAB provides mathematical *expressions*, but unlike most programming languages, these expressions involve entire matrices. The building blocks of expressions are:

- Variables
- Numbers
- Operators
- Functions

Variables

MATLAB does not require any type declarations or dimension statements. When MATLAB encounters a new variable name, it automatically creates the variable and allocates the appropriate amount of storage. If the variable already exists, MATLAB changes its contents and, if necessary, allocates new storage. For example,

```
num_students = 25
```

creates a 1-by-1 matrix named `num_students` and stores the value 25 in its single element.

Variable names consist of a letter, followed by any number of letters, digits, or underscores. MATLAB uses only the first 31 characters of a variable name. MATLAB is case sensitive; it distinguishes between uppercase and lowercase letters. A and a are *not* the same variable. To view the matrix assigned to any variable, simply enter the variable name.

Numbers

MATLAB uses conventional decimal notation, with an optional decimal point and leading plus or minus sign, for numbers. *Scientific notation* uses the letter e to specify a power-of-ten scale factor. *Imaginary numbers* use either i or j as a suffix. Some examples of legal numbers are

```
3              -99           0.0001
9.6397238      1.60210e-20   6.02252e23
1i             -3.14159j     3e5i
```

All numbers are stored internally using the *long* format specified by the IEEE floating-point standard. Floating-point numbers have a finite *precision* of roughly 16 significant decimal digits and a finite *range* of roughly 10^{-308} to 10^{+308}.

Operators

Expressions use familiar arithmetic operators and precedence rules.

+	Addition
-	Subtraction
*	Multiplication
/	Division
\	Left division (described in "Matrices and Linear Algebra" in *Using MATLAB*)
^	Power
'	Complex conjugate transpose
( )	Specify evaluation order

Functions

MATLAB provides a large number of standard elementary mathematical functions, including abs, sqrt, exp, and sin. Taking the square root or logarithm of a negative number is not an error; the appropriate complex result is produced automatically. MATLAB also provides many more advanced mathematical functions, including Bessel and gamma functions. Most of these functions accept complex arguments. For a list of the elementary mathematical functions, type

```
help elfun
```

For a list of more advanced mathematical and matrix functions, type

```
help specfun
help elmat
```

For More Information Appendix A, "MATLAB Quick Reference," contains brief descriptions of the MATLAB functions. Use the Help Desk to access complete descriptions of all the MATLAB functions by Subject or by Index.

Some of the functions, like sqrt and sin, are *built-in*. They are part of the MATLAB core so they are very efficient, but the computational details are not readily accessible. Other functions, like gamma and sinh, are implemented in M-files. You can see the code and even modify it if you want.

Several special functions provide values of useful constants.

pi	3.14159265...
i	Imaginary unit, $\sqrt{-1}$
j	Same as i
eps	Floating-point relative precision, 2^{-52}
realmin	Smallest floating-point number, 2^{-1022}
realmax	Largest floating-point number, $(2-\varepsilon)2^{1023}$
Inf	Infinity
NaN	Not-a-number

Infinity is generated by dividing a nonzero value by zero, or by evaluating well defined mathematical expressions that *overflow*, i.e., exceed realmax. Not-a-number is generated by trying to evaluate expressions like 0/0 or Inf-Inf that do not have well defined mathematical values.

The function names are not reserved. It is possible to overwrite any of them with a new variable, such as

```
eps = 1.e-6
```

and then use that value in subsequent calculations. The original function can be restored with

```
clear eps
```

Expressions

You have already seen several examples of MATLAB expressions. Here are a few more examples, and the resulting values.

```
rho = (1+sqrt(5))/2
rho =
    1.6180

a = abs(3+4i)
a =
    5

z = sqrt(besselk(4/3,rho-i))
z =
   0.3730+ 0.3214i

huge = exp(log(realmax))
huge =
  1.7977e+308

toobig = pi*huge
toobig =
    Inf
```

Working with Matrices

This section introduces you to other ways of creating matrices.

Generating Matrices

MATLAB provides four functions that generate basic matrices.

zeros	All zeros
ones	All ones
rand	Uniformly distributed random elements
randn	Normally distributed random elements

Here are some examples.

```
Z = zeros(2,4)
Z =
    0    0    0    0
    0    0    0    0

F = 5*ones(3,3)
F =
    5    5    5
    5    5    5
    5    5    5

N = fix(10*rand(1,10))
N =
    4    9    4    4    8    5    2    6    8    0

R = randn(4,4)
R =
    1.0668    0.2944   -0.6918   -1.4410
    0.0593   -1.3362    0.8580    0.5711
   -0.0956    0.7143    1.2540   -0.3999
   -0.8323    1.6236   -1.5937    0.6900
```

The load Command

The load command reads binary files containing matrices generated by earlier MATLAB sessions, or reads text files containing numeric data. The text file should be organized as a rectangular table of numbers, separated by blanks, with one row per line, and an equal number of elements in each row. For example, outside of MATLAB, create a text file containing these four lines.

```
16.0     3.0     2.0    13.0
 5.0    10.0    11.0     8.0
 9.0     6.0     7.0    12.0
 4.0    15.0    14.0     1.0
```

Store the file under the name magik.dat. Then the command

```
load magik.dat
```

reads the file and creates a variable, magik, containing our example matrix.

M-Files

You can create your own matrices using *M-files*, which are text files containing MATLAB code. Just create a file containing the same statements you would type at the MATLAB command line. Save the file under a name that ends in .m.

Note To access a text editor on a PC, choose **Open** or **New** from the **File** menu or press the appropriate button on the toolbar. To access a text editor under Linux, use the ! symbol followed by whatever command you would ordinarily use at your operating system prompt.

For example, create a file containing these five lines.

```
A = [ ...
16.0     3.0     2.0    13.0
 5.0    10.0    11.0     8.0
 9.0     6.0     7.0    12.0
 4.0    15.0    14.0     1.0 ];
```

Store the file under the name magik.m. Then the statement

    magik

reads the file and creates a variable, A, containing our example matrix.

Concatenation

Concatenation is the process of joining small matrices to make bigger ones. In fact, you made your first matrix by concatenating its individual elements. The pair of square brackets, [ ], is the concatenation operator. For an example, start with the 4-by-4 magic square, A, and form

    B = [A A+32; A+48 A+16]

The result is an 8-by-8 matrix, obtained by joining the four submatrices.

    B =

        16   3   2   13   48   35   34   45
         5   10   11   8   37   42   43   40
         9   6   7   12   41   38   39   44
         4   15   14   1   36   47   46   33
        64   51   50   61   32   19   18   29
        53   58   59   56   21   26   27   24
        57   54   55   60   25   22   23   28
        52   63   62   49   20   31   30   17

This matrix is half way to being another magic square. Its elements are a rearrangement of the integers 1:64. Its column sums are the correct value for an 8-by-8 magic square.

    sum(B)

    ans =
       260   260   260   260   260   260   260   260

But its row sums, sum(B')', are not all the same. Further manipulation is necessary to make this a valid 8-by-8 magic square.

Deleting Rows and Columns

You can delete rows and columns from a matrix using just a pair of square brackets. Start with

```
X = A;
```

Then, to delete the second column of X, use

```
X(:,2) = []
```

This changes X to

```
X =
      16      2     13
       5     11      8
       9      7     12
       4     14      1
```

If you delete a single element from a matrix, the result isn't a matrix anymore. So, expressions like

```
X(1,2) = []
```

result in an error. However, using a single subscript deletes a single element, or sequence of elements, and reshapes the remaining elements into a row vector. So

```
X(2:2:10) = []
```

results in

```
X =
      16      9      2      7     13     12      1
```

More About Matrices and Arrays

This sections shows you more about working with matrices and arrays, focusing on:

- Linear algebra
- Arrays
- Multivariate data

Linear Algebra

Informally, the terms *matrix* and *array* are often used interchangeably. More precisely, a *matrix* is a two-dimensional numeric array that represents a *linear transformation*. The mathematical operations defined on matrices are the subject of *linear algebra*.

Dürer's magic square

```
A =
    16     3     2    13
     5    10    11     8
     9     6     7    12
     4    15    14     1
```

provides several examples that give a taste of MATLAB matrix operations. You've already seen the matrix transpose, A'. Adding a matrix to its transpose produces a *symmetric* matrix.

```
A + A'

ans =
    32     8    11    17
     8    20    17    23
    11    17    14    26
    17    23    26     2
```

For More Information All of the MATLAB math functions are described in the *MATLAB Function Reference*, which is accessible from the Help Desk.

The multiplication symbol, *, denotes the *matrix* multiplication involving inner products between rows and columns. Multiplying the transpose of a matrix by the original matrix also produces a symmetric matrix.

```
A'*A

ans =
    378   212   206   360
    212   370   368   206
    206   368   370   212
    360   206   212   378
```

The determinant of this particular matrix happens to be zero, indicating that the matrix is *singular*.

```
d = det(A)

d =
    0
```

The reduced row echelon form of A is not the identity.

```
R = rref(A)

R =
    1    0    0    1
    0    1    0   -3
    0    0    1    3
    0    0    0    0
```

Since the matrix is singular, it does not have an inverse. If you try to compute the inverse with

```
X = inv(A)
```

you will get a warning message

```
Warning: Matrix is close to singular or badly scaled.
         Results may be inaccurate. RCOND = 1.175530e-017.
```

Roundoff error has prevented the matrix inversion algorithm from detecting exact singularity. But the value of rcond, which stands for *reciprocal condition estimate*, is on the order of eps, the floating-point relative precision, so the computed inverse is unlikely to be of much use.

The eigenvalues of the magic square are interesting.

```
e = eig(A)

e =
    34.0000
     8.0000
     0.0000
    -8.0000
```

One of the eigenvalues is zero, which is another consequence of singularity. The largest eigenvalue is 34, the magic sum. That's because the vector of all ones is an eigenvector.

```
v = ones(4,1)

v =
     1
     1
     1
     1

A*v

ans =
    34
    34
    34
    34
```

When a magic square is scaled by its magic sum,

```
P = A/34
```

the result is a *doubly stochastic* matrix whose row and column sums are all one.

```
P =
    0.4706    0.0882    0.0588    0.3824
    0.1471    0.2941    0.3235    0.2353
    0.2647    0.1765    0.2059    0.3529
    0.1176    0.4412    0.4118    0.0294
```

Such matrices represent the transition probabilities in a *Markov process*. Repeated powers of the matrix represent repeated steps of the process. For our example, the fifth power

    P^5

is

       0.2507   0.2495   0.2494   0.2504
       0.2497   0.2501   0.2502   0.2500
       0.2500   0.2498   0.2499   0.2503
       0.2496   0.2506   0.2505   0.2493

This shows that as k approaches infinity, all the elements in the kth power, P^k, approach ¼.

Finally, the coefficients in the characteristic polynomial

    poly(A)

are

       1   -34   -64   2176   0

This indicates that the characteristic polynomial

    $\det(A - \lambda I)$

is

   $\lambda^4 - 34\lambda^3 - 64\lambda^2 + 2176\lambda$

The constant term is zero, because the matrix is singular, and the coefficient of the cubic term is -34, because the matrix is magic!

Arrays

When they are taken away from the world of linear algebra, matrices become two dimensional numeric arrays. Arithmetic operations on arrays are done element-by-element. This means that addition and subtraction are the same for arrays and matrices, but that multiplicative operations are different. MATLAB uses a dot, or decimal point, as part of the notation for multiplicative array operations.

The list of operators includes:

+	Addition
-	Subtraction
.*	Element-by-element multiplication
./	Element-by-element division
.\	Element-by-element left division
.^	Element-by-element power
.'	Unconjugated array transpose

If the Dürer magic square is multiplied by itself with array multiplication

```
A.*A
```

the result is an array containing the squares of the integers from 1 to 16, in an unusual order.

```
ans =
    256      9      4    169
     25    100    121     64
     81     36     49    144
     16    225    196      1
```

Array operations are useful for building tables. Suppose n is the column vector

```
n = (0:9)';
```

Then

```
pows = [n  n.^2  2.^n]
```

builds a table of squares and powers of two.

```
pows =
     0     0     1
     1     1     2
     2     4     4
     3     9     8
     4    16    16
     5    25    32
     6    36    64
     7    49   128
     8    64   256
     9    81   512
```

The elementary math functions operate on arrays element by element. So

```
format short g
x = (1:0.1:2)';
logs = [x log10(x)]
```

builds a table of logarithms.

```
logs =
     1.0            0
     1.1      0.04139
     1.2      0.07918
     1.3      0.11394
     1.4      0.14613
     1.5      0.17609
     1.6      0.20412
     1.7      0.23045
     1.8      0.25527
     1.9      0.27875
     2.0      0.30103
```

Multivariate Data

MATLAB uses column-oriented analysis for multivariate statistical data. Each column in a data set represents a variable and each row an observation. The (i,j)th element is the ith observation of the jth variable.

As an example, consider a data set with three variables:

- Heart rate
- Weight
- Hours of exercise per week

For five observations, the resulting array might look like

```
D =
        72              134             3.2
        81              201             3.5
        69              156             7.1
        82              148             2.4
        75              170             1.2
```

The first row contains the heart rate, weight, and exercise hours for patient 1, the second row contains the data for patient 2, and so on. Now you can apply many of MATLAB's data analysis functions to this data set. For example, to obtain the mean and standard deviation of each column:

```
mu = mean(D), sigma = std(D)

mu =
      75.8           161.8            3.48

sigma =
      5.6303          25.499          2.2107
```

For a list of the data analysis functions available in MATLAB, type

```
help datafun
```

If you have access to the Statistics Toolbox, type

```
help stats
```

Scalar Expansion

Matrices and scalars can be combined in several different ways. For example, a scalar is subtracted from a matrix by subtracting it from each element. The average value of the elements in our magic square is 8.5, so

```
B = A - 8.5
```

forms a matrix whose column sums are zero.

```
B =
        7.5      -5.5      -6.5       4.5
       -3.5       1.5       2.5      -0.5
        0.5      -2.5      -1.5       3.5
       -4.5       6.5       5.5      -7.5

sum(B)

ans =
     0     0     0     0
```

With scalar expansion, MATLAB assigns a specified scalar to all indices in a range. For example,

```
B(1:2,2:3) = 0
```

zeros out a portion of B

```
B =
        7.5         0         0       4.5
       -3.5         0         0      -0.5
        0.5      -2.5      -1.5       3.5
       -4.5       6.5       5.5      -7.5
```

Logical Subscripting

The logical vectors created from logical and relational operations can be used to reference subarrays. Suppose X is an ordinary matrix and L is a matrix of the same size that is the result of some logical operation. Then X(L) specifies the elements of X where the elements of L are nonzero.

This kind of subscripting can be done in one step by specifying the logical operation as the subscripting expression. Suppose you have the following set of data.

```
x =
    2.1 1.7 1.6 1.5 NaN 1.9 1.8 1.5 5.1 1.8 1.4 2.2 1.6 1.8
```

The NaN is a marker for a missing observation, such as a failure to respond to an item on a questionnaire. To remove the missing data with logical indexing, use finite(x), which is true for all finite numerical values and false for NaN and Inf.

```
x = x(finite(x))
x =
   2.1 1.7 1.6 1.5 1.9 1.8 1.5 5.1 1.8 1.4 2.2 1.6 1.8
```

Now there is one observation, 5.1, which seems to be very different from the others. It is an *outlier*. The following statement removes outliers, in this case those elements more than three standard deviations from the mean.

```
x = x(abs(x-mean(x)) <= 3*std(x))
x =
   2.1 1.7 1.6 1.5 1.9 1.8 1.5 1.8 1.4 2.2 1.6 1.8
```

For another example, highlight the location of the prime numbers in Dürer's magic square by using logical indexing and scalar expansion to set the nonprimes to 0.

```
A(~isprime(A)) = 0

A =
     0     3     2    13
     5     0    11     0
     0     0     7     0
     0     0     0     0
```

The find Function

The find function determines the indices of array elements that meet a given logical condition. In its simplest form, find returns a column vector of indices. Transpose that vector to obtain a row vector of indices. For example,

```
k = find(isprime(A))'
```

picks out the locations, using one-dimensional indexing, of the primes in the magic square.

```
k =
     2     5     9    10    11    13
```

Display those primes, as a row vector in the order determined by k, with

```
A(k)
```

```
ans =
     5     3     2    11     7    13
```

When you use k as a left-hand-side index in an assignment statement, the matrix structure is preserved.

```
A(k) = NaN
```

```
A =
    16   NaN   NaN   NaN
   NaN    10   NaN     8
     9     6   NaN    12
     4    15    14     1
```

The Command Window

So far, you have been using the MATLAB command line, typing commands and expressions, and seeing the results printed in the command window. This section describes a few ways of altering the appearance of the command window. If your system allows you to select the command window font or typeface, we recommend you use a fixed width font, such as Fixedsys or Courier, to provide proper spacing.

The format Command

The format command controls the numeric format of the values displayed by MATLAB. The command affects only how numbers are displayed, not how MATLAB computes or saves them. Here are the different formats, together with the resulting output produced from a vector x with components of different magnitudes.

```
x = [4/3 1.2345e-6]

format short

    1.3333    0.0000

format short e

    1.3333e+000   1.2345e-006

format short g

    1.3333   1.2345e-006

format long

    1.33333333333333    0.00000123450000

format long e

    1.333333333333333e+000    1.234500000000000e-006
```

```
format long g

    1.33333333333333                    1.2345e-006

format bank

    1.33           0.00

format rat

    4/3           1/810045

format hex

    3ff5555555555555    3eb4b6231abfd271
```

If the largest element of a matrix is larger than 10^3 or smaller than 10^{-3}, MATLAB applies a common scale factor for the short and long formats.

In addition to the format commands shown above

```
format compact
```

suppresses many of the blank lines that appear in the output. This lets you view more information on a screen or window. If you want more control over the output format, use the sprintf and fprintf functions.

Suppressing Output

If you simply type a statement and press **Return** or **Enter**, MATLAB automatically displays the results on screen. However, if you end the line with a semicolon, MATLAB performs the computation but does not display any output. This is particularly useful when you generate large matrices. For example,

```
A = magic(100);
```

Long Command Lines

If a statement does not fit on one line, use three periods, . . . , followed by **Return** or **Enter** to indicate that the statement continues on the next line. For example,

```
s = 1 -1/2 + 1/3 -1/4 + 1/5 - 1/6 + 1/7 ...
      - 1/8 + 1/9 - 1/10 + 1/11 - 1/12;
```

Blank spaces around the =, +, and - signs are optional, but they improve readability.

Command Line Editing

Various arrow and control keys on your keyboard allow you to recall, edit, and reuse commands you have typed earlier. For example, suppose you mistakenly enter

```
rho = (1 + sqt(5))/2
```

You have misspelled sqrt. MATLAB responds with

```
Undefined function or variable 'sqt'.
```

Instead of retyping the entire line, simply press the ↑ key. The misspelled command is redisplayed. Use the ← key to move the cursor over and insert the missing r. Repeated use of the ↑ key recalls earlier lines. Typing a few characters and then the ↑ key finds a previous line that begins with those characters.

The list of available command line editing keys is different on different computers. Experiment to see which of the following keys is available on your machine. (Many of these keys will be familiar to users of the EMACS editor.)

↑	**Ctrl-p**	Recall previous line
↓	**Ctrl-n**	Recall next line
←	**Ctrl-b**	Move back one character
→	**Ctrl-f**	Move forward one character
Ctrl-→	**Ctrl-r**	Move right one word

Ctrl-←	**Ctrl-l**	Move left one word
Home	**Ctrl-a**	Move to beginning of line
End	**Ctrl-e**	Move to end of line
Esc	**Ctrl-u**	Clear line
Del	**Ctrl-d**	Delete character at cursor
Backspace	**Ctrl-h**	Delete character before cursor
	Ctrl-k	Delete to end of line

The MATLAB Environment

The MATLAB environment includes both the set of variables built up during a MATLAB session and the set of disk files containing programs and data that persist between sessions.

The Workspace

The *workspace* is the area of memory accessible from the MATLAB command line. Two commands, who and whos, show the current contents of the workspace. The who command gives a short list, while whos also gives size and storage information.

Here is the output produced by whos on a workspace containing results from some of the examples in this book. It shows several different MATLAB data structures. As an exercise, you might see if you can match each of the variables with the code segment in this book that generates it.

```
whos

    Name        Size          Bytes  Class

    A           4x4             128   double array
    D           5x3             120   double array
    M           10x1           3816   cell array
    S           1x3             442   struct array
    h           1x11             22   char array
    n           1x1               8   double array
    s           1x5              10   char array
    v           2x5              20   char array

Grand total is 471 elements using 4566 bytes.
```

To delete all the existing variables from the workspace, enter

```
clear
```

save Commands

The save commands preserve the contents of the workspace in a MAT-file that can be read with the load command in a later MATLAB session. For example,

```
save August17th
```

saves the entire workspace contents in the file August17th.mat. If desired, you can save only certain variables by specifying the variable names after the filename.

Ordinarily, the variables are saved in a binary format that can be read quickly (and accurately) by MATLAB. If you want to access these files outside of MATLAB, you may want to specify an alternative format.

-ascii	Use 8-digit text format.
-ascii -double	Use 16-digit text format.
-ascii -double -tabs	Delimit array elements with tabs.
-v4	Create a file for MATLAB version 4.
-append	Append data to an existing MAT-file.

When you save workspace contents in text format, you should save only one variable at a time. If you save more than one variable, MATLAB will create the text file, but you will be unable to load it easily back into MATLAB.

The Search Path

MATLAB uses a search path, an ordered list of directories, to determine how to execute the functions you call. When you call a standard function, MATLAB executes the first M-file function on the path that has the specified name. You can override this behavior using special private directories and subfunctions.

The command

```
path
```

shows the search path on any platform. On PCs, choose **Set Path** from the **File** menu to view or modify the path.

Disk File Manipulation

The commands `dir`, `type`, `delete`, and `cd` implement a set of generic operating system commands for manipulating files. This table indicates how these commands map to other operating systems.

MATLAB	MS-DOS	Linux
dir	dir	ls
type	type	cat
delete	del or erase	rm
cd	chdir	cd

For most of these commands, you can use pathnames, wildcards, and drive designators in the usual way.

The diary Command

The `diary` command creates a diary of your MATLAB session in a disk file. You can view and edit the resulting text file using any word processor. To create a file called `diary` that contains all the commands you enter, as well as MATLAB's printed output (but not the graphics output), enter

```
diary
```

To save the MATLAB session in a file with a particular name, use

```
diary filename
```

To stop recording the session, use

```
diary off
```

Running External Programs

The exclamation point character ! is a shell escape and indicates that the rest of the input line is a command to the operating system. This is quite useful for invoking utilities or running other programs without quitting MATLAB. On Linux, for example,

```
!emacs magik.m
```

invokes an editor called emacs for a file named magik.m. When you quit the external program, the operating system returns control to MATLAB.

Help and Online Documentation

There are several different ways to access online information about MATLAB functions:

- The MATLAB Help Desk
- Online reference pages
- The help command
- Link to The MathWorks, Inc.

The Help Desk

The MATLAB Help Desk provides access to a wide range of help and reference information stored on CD. Many of the underlying documents use HyperText Markup Language (HTML) and are accessed with an Internet Web browser such as Netscape or Microsoft Explorer. The Help Desk process can be started on PCs by selecting the **Help Desk** option under the **Help** menu, or, on all computers, by typing

```
helpdesk
```

All of MATLAB's operators and functions have online reference pages in HTML format, which you can reach from the Help Desk. These pages provide more details and examples than the basic help entries. HTML versions of other documents, including this manual, are also available. A search engine, running on your own machine, can query all the online reference material.

Using the Help Desk

When you access the Help Desk, you see its entry screen.

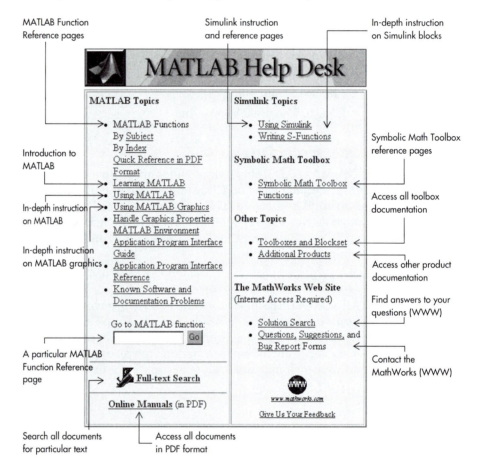

MATLAB Function
Reference pages

Simulink instruction
and reference pages

In-depth instruction
on Simulink blocks

Introduction to
MATLAB

In-depth instruction
on MATLAB

In-depth instruction
on MATLAB graphics

A particular MATLAB
Function Reference
page

Symbolic Math Toolbox
reference pages

Access all toolbox
documentation

Access other product
documentation

Find answers to your
questions (WWW)

Contact the
MathWorks (WWW)

Search all documents
for particular text

Access all documents
in PDF format

Online Reference Pages

The doc Command

If you know the name of a specific function, you can view its reference page
directly. For example, to get the reference page for the eval function, type

```
doc eval
```

The doc command starts your Web browser, if it is not already running.

Printing Online Reference Pages

Versions of the online reference pages, as well as the rest of the MATLAB documentation set, are also available in Portable Document Format (PDF) through the Help Desk. These pages are processed by Adobe's Acrobat reader. They reproduce the look and feel of the printed page, complete with fonts, graphics, formatting, and images. This is the best way to get printed copies of reference material. To access the PDF versions of the books, select **Online Manuals** from the Help Desk and then choose the desired book.

The help Command

The help command is the most basic way to determine the syntax and behavior of a particular function. Information is displayed directly in the command window. For example,

```
help magic
```

prints

```
MAGIC  Magic square.
    MAGIC(N) is an N-by-N matrix constructed from
    the integers 1 through N^2 with equal row,
    column, and diagonal sums.
    Produces valid magic squares for N = 1,3,4,5....
```

Note MATLAB online help entries use uppercase characters for the function and variable names to make them stand out from the rest of the text. When typing function names, however, always use the corresponding lowercase characters because MATLAB is case sensitive and all function names are actually in lowercase.

All the MATLAB functions are organized into logical groups, and MATLAB's directory structure is based on this grouping. For example, all the linear algebra functions reside in the `matfun` directory. To list the names of all the functions in that directory, with a brief description of each

```
help matfun

Matrix functions - numerical linear algebra.

Matrix analysis.
  norm        - Matrix or vector norm.
  normest     - Estimate the matrix 2-norm
...
```

The command

```
help
```

by itself lists all the directories, with a description of the function category each represents.

```
matlab/general
matlab/ops
...
```

The lookfor Command

The `lookfor` command allows you to search for functions based on a keyword. It searches through the first line of `help` text, which is known as the H1 line, for each MATLAB function, and returns the H1 lines containing a specified keyword. For example, MATLAB does not have a function named `inverse`. So the response from

```
help inverse
```

is

```
inverse.m not found.
```

But

```
lookfor inverse
```

finds over a dozen matches. Depending on which toolboxes you have installed, you will find entries like

```
INVHILB Inverse Hilbert matrix.
ACOSH   Inverse hyperbolic cosine.
ERFINV  Inverse of the error function.
INV     Matrix inverse.
PINV    Pseudoinverse.
IFFT    Inverse discrete Fourier transform.
IFFT2   Two-dimensional inverse discrete Fourier transform.
ICCEPS  Inverse complex cepstrum.
IDCT    Inverse discrete cosine transform.
```

Adding -all to the lookfor command, as in

```
lookfor -all
```

searches the entire help entry, not just the H1 line.

Link to the MathWorks

If your computer is connected to the Internet, the Help Desk provides a connection to The MathWorks, the home of MATLAB. You can also use the Solution Search Engine at The MathWorks Web site to query an up-to-date data base of technical support information.

4

Graphics

Basic Plotting

MATLAB has extensive facilities for displaying vectors and matrices as graphs, as well as annotating and printing these graphs. This section describes a few of the most important graphics functions and provides examples of some typical applications.

For More Information *Using MATLAB Graphics* provides in-depth coverage of MATLAB graphics and visualization tools. Access *Using MATLAB Graphics* from the Help Desk.

Creating a Plot

The plot function has different forms, depending on the input arguments. If y is a vector, plot(y) produces a piecewise linear graph of the elements of y versus the index of the elements of y. If you specify two vectors as arguments, plot(x,y) produces a graph of y versus x.

For example, these statements use the colon operator to create a vector of x values ranging from zero to 2π, compute the sine of these values, and plot the result.

```
x = 0:pi/100:2*pi;
y = sin(x);
plot(x,y)
```

Now label the axes and add a title. The characters \pi create the symbol π.

```
xlabel('x = 0:2\pi')
ylabel('Sine of x')
title('Plot of the Sine Function','FontSize',12)
```

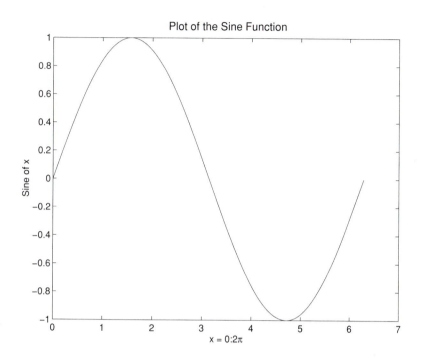

Multiple Data Sets in One Graph

Multiple x-y pair arguments create multiple graphs with a single call to plot. MATLAB automatically cycles through a predefined (but user settable) list of colors to allow discrimination between each set of data. For example, these statements plot three related functions of x, each curve in a separate distinguishing color.

```
y2 = sin(x-.25);
y3 = sin(x-.5);
plot(x,y,x,y2,x,y3)
```

The legend command provides an easy way to identify the individual plots.

```
legend('sin(x)','sin(x-.25)','sin(x-.5)')
```

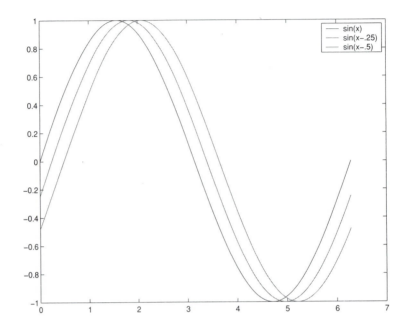

For More Information See "Defining the Color of Lines for Plotting" in the Axes Properties chapter of *Using MATLAB Graphics*. Access *Using MATLAB Graphics* from the Help Desk.

Specifying Line Styles and Colors

It is possible to specify color, line styles, and markers (such as plus signs or circles) with the syntax

```
plot(x,y,'color_style_marker')
```

color_style_marker is a string containing from one to four characters (enclosed in single quotation marks) constructed from a color, a line style, and a marker type:

- Color strings are 'c', 'm', 'y', 'r', 'g', 'b', 'w', and 'k'. These correspond to cyan, magenta, yellow, red, green, blue, white, and black.
- Linestyle strings are '-' for solid, '--' for dashed, ':' for dotted, '-.' for dash-dot, and 'none' for no line.
- The marker types are '+', 'o', '*', and 'x' and the filled marker types 's' for square, 'd' for diamond, '^' for up triangle, 'v' for down triangle, '>' for right triangle, '<' for left triangle, 'p' for pentagram, 'h' for hexagram, and none for no marker.

Plotting Lines and Markers

If you specify a marker type but not a linestyle, MATLAB draws only the marker. For example,

```
plot(x,y,'ks')
```

plots black squares at each data point, but does not connect the markers with a line.

The statement

```
plot(x,y,'r:+')
```

plots a red dotted line and places plus sign markers at each data point. You may want to use fewer data points to plot the markers than you use to plot the lines. This example plots the data twice using a different number of points for the dotted line and marker plots.

```
x1 = 0:pi/100:2*pi;
x2 = 0:pi/10:2*pi;
plot(x1,sin(x1),'r:',x2,sin(x2),'r+')
```

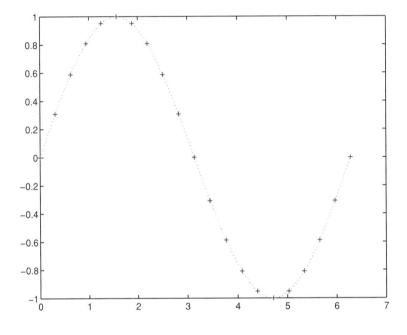

For More Information See the "Basic Plotting" chapter of *Using MATLAB Graphics* for more examples of plotting options. Access *Using MATLAB Graphics* from the Help Desk.

Imaginary and Complex Data

When the arguments to plot are complex, the imaginary part is ignored *except* when plot is given a single complex argument. For this special case, the command is a shortcut for a plot of the real part versus the imaginary part. Therefore,

```
plot(Z)
```

where Z is a complex vector or matrix, is equivalent to

```
plot(real(Z),imag(Z))
```

For example,

```
t = 0:pi/10:2*pi;
plot(exp(i*t),'-o')
axis equal
```

draws a 20-sided polygon with little circles at the vertices. The command, axis equal, makes the individual tick mark increments on the x- and y-axes the same length, which makes this plot more circular in appearance.

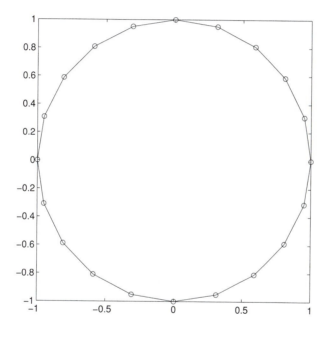

Adding Plots to an Existing Graph

The hold command enables you to add plots to an existing graph. When you type

```
hold on
```

MATLAB does not replace the existing graph when you issue another plotting command; it adds the new data to the current graph, rescaling the axes if necessary.

For example, these statements first create a contour plot of the peaks function, then superimpose a pseudocolor plot of the same function.

```
[x,y,z] = peaks;
contour(x,y,z,20,'k')
hold on
pcolor(x,y,z)
shading interp
hold off
```

The hold on command causes the pcolor plot to be combined with the contour plot in one figure.

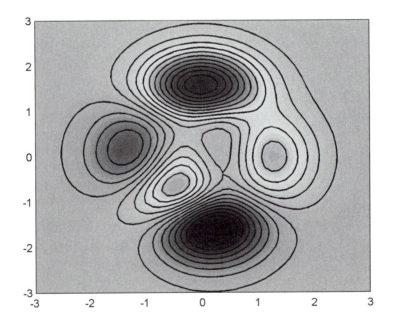

For More Information See the "Specialized Graphs" chapter in *Using MATLAB Graphics* for information on a variety of graph types. Access *Using MATLAB Graphics* from the Help Desk.

Figure Windows

Graphing functions automatically open a new figure window if there are no figure windows already on the screen. If a figure window exists, MATLAB uses that window for graphics output. If there are multiple figure windows open, MATLAB targets the one that is designated the "current figure" (the last figure used or clicked in).

To make an existing figure window the current figure, you can click the mouse while the pointer is in that window or you can type

```
figure(n)
```

where n is the number in the figure title bar. The results of subsequent graphics commands are displayed in this window.

To open a new figure window and make it the current figure, type

```
figure
```

For More Information See the "Figure Properties" chapter in *Using MATLAB Graphics* and the reference page for the figure command. Access *Using MATLAB Graphics* and the figure reference page from the Help Desk.

Multiple Plots in One Figure

The subplot command enables you to display multiple plots in the same window or print them on the same piece of paper. Typing

```
subplot(m,n,p)
```

partitions the figure window into an m-by-n matrix of small subplots and selects the pth subplot for the current plot. The plots are numbered along first the top row of the figure window, then the second row, and so on. For example, these statements plot data in four different subregions of the figure window.

```
t = 0:pi/10:2*pi;
[X,Y,Z] = cylinder(4*cos(t));
subplot(2,2,1); mesh(X)
subplot(2,2,2); mesh(Y)
subplot(2,2,3); mesh(Z)
subplot(2,2,4); mesh(X,Y,Z)
```

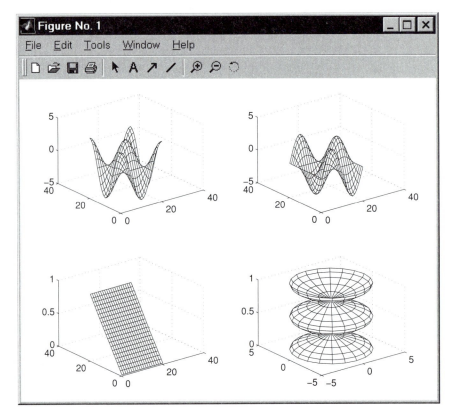

Controlling the Axes

The axis command supports a number of options for setting the scaling, orientation, and aspect ratio of plots.

Setting Axis Limits

By default, MATLAB finds the maxima and minima of the data to choose the axis limits to span this range. The axis command enables you to specify your own limits

```
axis([xmin xmax ymin ymax])
```

or for three-dimensional graphs,

```
axis([xmin xmax ymin ymax zmin zmax])
```

Use the command

```
axis auto
```

to re-enable MATLAB's automatic limit selection.

Setting Axis Aspect Ratio

axis also enables you to specify a number of predefined modes. For example,

```
axis square
```

makes the x-axes and y-axes the same length.

```
axis equal
```

makes the individual tick mark increments on the x- and y-axes the same length. This means

```
plot(exp(i*[0:pi/10:2*pi]))
```

followed by either axis square or axis equal turns the oval into a proper circle.

```
axis auto normal
```

returns the axis scaling to its default, automatic mode.

Setting Axis Visibility

You can use the `axis` command to make the axis visible or invisible.

    axis on

makes the axis visible. This is the default.

    axis off

makes the axis invisible.

Setting Grid Lines

The `grid` command toggles grid lines on and off. The statement

    grid on

turns the grid lines on and

    grid off

turns them back off again.

For More Information See the `axis` and `axes` reference pages and the "Axes Properties" chapter in *Using MATLAB Graphics*. Access these reference pages and *Using MATLAB Graphics* from the Help Desk.

Axis Labels and Titles

The `xlabel`, `ylabel`, and `zlabel` commands add x-, y-, and z-axis labels. The `title` command adds a title at the top of the figure and the `text` function inserts text anywhere in the figure. A subset of TeX notation produces Greek letters.

    t = -pi:pi/100:pi;
    y = sin(t);
    plot(t,y)
    axis([-pi pi -1 1])
    xlabel('-\pi \leq {\itt} \leq \pi')
    ylabel('sin(t)')
    title('Graph of the sine function')
    text(1,-1/3,'{\itNote the odd symmetry.}')

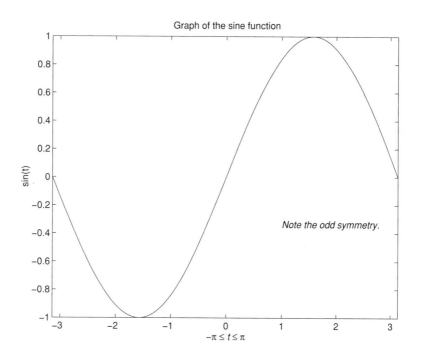

For More Information See the "Labeling Graphs" chapter in *Using MATLAB Graphics* for more information. Access *Using MATLAB Graphics* from the Help Desk.

Annotating Plots Using the Plot Editor

After creating a plot, you can make changes to it and annotate it with the Plot Editor, which is an easy-to-use graphical interface. The following illustration

shows the plot in a figure window and labels the main features of the figure
window and the Plot Editor.

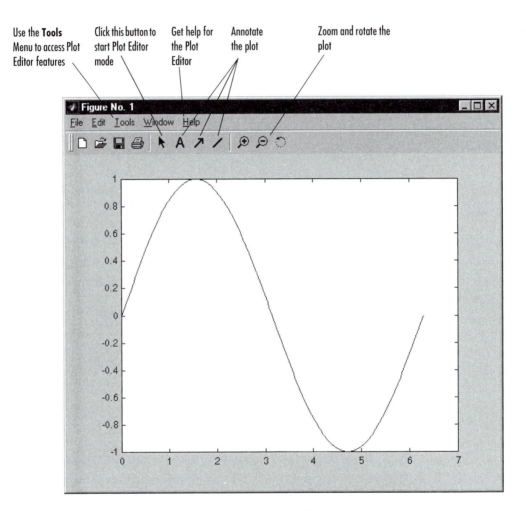

Use the **Tools**
Menu to access Plot
Editor features

Click this button to
start Plot Editor
mode

Get help for
the Plot
Editor

Annotate
the plot

Zoom and rotate the
plot

To save a figure, select **Save** from the **File** menu. To save it using a graphics
format, such as TIFF, for use with other applications, select **Export** from the
File menu. You can also save from the command line – use the saveas
command, including any options to save the figure in a different format.

Mesh and Surface Plots

MATLAB defines a surface by the z-coordinates of points above a grid in the x-y plane, using straight lines to connect adjacent points. The mesh and surf plotting functions display surfaces in three dimensions. mesh produces wireframe surfaces that color only the lines connecting the defining points. surf displays both the connecting lines and the faces of the surface in color.

Visualizing Functions of Two Variables

To display a function of two variables, $z = f(x,y)$:

- Generate X and Y matrices consisting of repeated rows and columns, respectively, over the domain of the function.
- Use X and Y to evaluate and graph the function.

The meshgrid function transforms the domain specified by a single vector or two vectors x and y into matrices X and Y for use in evaluating functions of two variables. The rows of X are copies of the vector x and the columns of Y are copies of the vector y.

Example – Graphing the sinc Function

This example evaluates and graphs the two-dimensional *sinc* function, $\sin(r)/r$, between the x and y directions. R is the distance from origin, which is at the center of the matrix. Adding eps (a MATLAB command that returns the smallest floating-point number on your system) avoids the indeterminate 0/0 at the origin.

```
[X,Y] = meshgrid(-8:.5:8);
R = sqrt(X.^2 + Y.^2) + eps;
Z = sin(R)./R;
mesh(X,Y,Z,'EdgeColor','black')
```

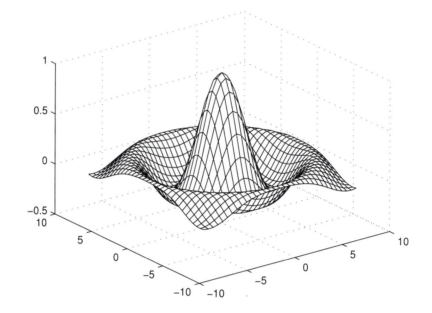

By default, MATLAB colors the mesh using the current colormap. However, this example uses a single-colored mesh by specifying the EdgeColor surface property. See the surface reference page for a list of all surface properties.

You can create a transparent mesh by disabling hidden line removal.

```
hidden off
```

See the hidden reference page for more information on this option.

Example – Colored Surface Plots

A surface plot is similar to a mesh plot except the rectangular faces of the surface are colored. The color of the faces is determined by the values of Z and the colormap (a colormap is an ordered list of colors). These statements graph the sinc function as a surface plot, select a colormap, and add a color bar to show the mapping of data to color.

```
surf(X,Y,Z)
colormap hsv
colorbar
```

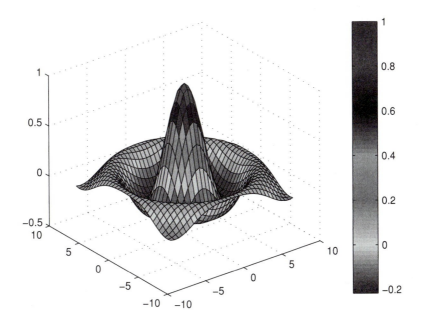

See the `colormap` reference page for information on colormaps.

For More Information See the "Creating 3-D Graphs" chapter in *Using MATLAB Graphics* for more information on surface plots. Access *Using MATLAB Graphics* from the Help Desk.

Surface Plots with Lighting

Lighting is the technique of illuminating an object with a directional light source. In certain cases, this technique can make subtle differences in surface shape easier to see. Lighting can also be used to add realism to three-dimensional graphs.

This example uses the same surface as the previous examples, but colors it red and removes the mesh lines. A light object is then added to the left of the "camera" (that is the location in space from where you are viewing the surface).

4-17

After adding the light and setting the lighting method to phong, use the view command to change the view point so you are looking at the surface from a different point in space (an azimuth of -15 and an elevation of 65 degrees). Finally, zoom in on the surface using the toolbar zoom mode.

```
surf(X,Y,Z,'FaceColor','red','EdgeColor','none');
camlight left; lighting phong
view(-15,65)
```

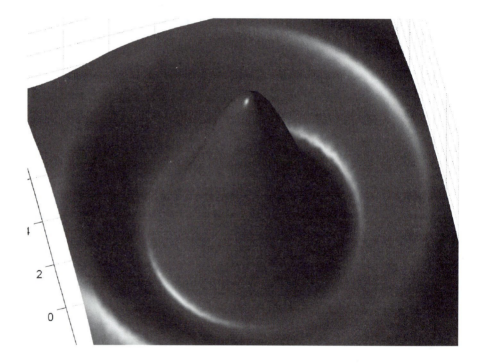

For More Information See the "Lighting as a Visualization Tool" and "Defining the View" chapters in *Using MATLAB Graphics* for information on these techniques. Access *Using MATLAB Graphics* from the Help Desk.

Images

Two-dimensional arrays can be displayed as *images*, where the array elements determine brightness or color of the images. For example, the statements

```
load durer
whos
Name          Size         Bytes   Class

  X           648x509     2638656   double array
  caption     2x28            112   char array
  map         128x3          3072   double array
```

load the file durer.mat, adding three variables to the workspace. The matrix X is a 648-by-509 matrix and map is a 128-by-3 matrix that is the colormap for this image.

Note MAT-files, such as durer.mat, are binary files that can be created on one platform and later read by MATLAB on a different platform.

The elements of X are integers between 1 and 128, which serve as indices into the colormap, map. Then

```
image(X)
colormap(map)
axis image
```

reproduces Dürer's etching shown at the beginning of this book. A high resolution scan of the magic square in the upper right corner is available in another file. Type

```
load detail
```

and then use the uparrow key on your keyboard to reexecute the image, colormap, and axis commands. The statement

```
colormap(hot)
```

adds some twentieth century colorization to the sixteenth century etching. The function hot generates a colormap containing shades of reds, oranges, and yellows. Typically a given image matrix has a specific colormap associated with it. See the `colormap` reference page for a list of other predefined colormaps.

For More Information See the "Displaying Bit-Mapped Images" chapter in *Using MATLAB Graphics* for information the image processing capabilities of MATLAB. Access *Using MATLAB Graphics* from the Help Desk.

Printing Graphics

You can print a MATLAB figure directly on a printer connected to your computer or you can export the figure to one of the standard graphic file formats supported by MATLAB. There are two ways to print and export figures:

- Using the **Print** option under the **File** menu
- Using the print command

Printing from the Menu

There are four menu options under the **File** menu that pertain to printing:

- The **Page Setup** option displays a dialog box that enables you to adjust characteristics of the figure on the printed page.
- The **Print Setup** option displays a dialog box that sets printing defaults, but does not actually print the figure.
- The **Print Preview** option enables you to view the figure the way it will look on the printed page.
- The **Print** option displays a dialog box that lets you select standard printing options and print the figure.

Generally, use **Print Preview** to determine whether the printed output is what you want. If not, use the **Page Setup** dialog box to change the output settings. The **Page Setup** dialog box **Help** button displays information on how to set up the page.

Exporting Figure to Graphics Files

The **Export** option under the **File** menu enables you to export the figure to a variety of standard graphics file formats.

Using the Print Command

The print command provides more flexibility in the type of output sent to the printer and allows you to control printing from M-files. The result can be sent directly to your default printer or stored in a specified file. A wide variety of output formats, including TIFF, JPEG, and PostScript, is available.

For example, this statement saves the contents of the current figure window as color Encapsulated Level 2 PostScript in the file called magicsquare.eps. It also includes a TIFF preview, which enables most word processors to display the picture

```
print -depsc2 -tiff magicsquare.eps
```

To save the same figure as a TIFF file with a resolution of 200 dpi, use the command

```
print -dtiff -r200 magicsquare.tiff
```

If you type print on the command line,

```
print
```

MATLAB prints the current figure on your default printer.

For More Information See the print command reference page and the "Printing MATLAB Graphics" chapter in *Using MATLAB Graphics* for more information on printing. Access this information from the Help Desk.

Handle Graphics

When you use a plotting command, MATLAB creates the graph using various graphics objects, such as lines, text, and surfaces (see Table 4-1 for a complete list). All graphics objects have properties that control the appearance and behavior of the object. MATLAB enables you to query the value of each property and set the value of most properties.

Whenever MATLAB creates a graphics object, it assigns an identifier (called a handle) to the object. You can use this handle to access the object's properties. Handle Graphics is useful if you want to:

- Modify the appearance of graphs.
- Create custom plotting commands by writing M-files that create and manipulate objects directly.

The material in this manual concentrates on modifying the appearance of graphs. See the "Handle Graphics" chapter in *Using MATLAB Graphics* for more information on programming with Handle Graphics.

Graphics Objects

Graphics objects are the basic elements used to display graphics and user interface elements. Table 4-1 lists the graphics objects.

Table 4-1: Handle Graphics Objects

Object	Description
Root	Top of the hierarchy corresponding to the computer screen
Figure	Window used to display graphics and user interfaces
Uicontrol	User interface control that executes a function in response to user interaction
Uimenu	User-defined figure window menu
Uicontextmenu	Pop-up menu invoked by right clicking on a graphics object

Table 4-1: Handle Graphics Objects (Continued)

Object	Description
Axes	Axes for displaying graphs in a figure
Image	Two-dimensional pixel-based picture
Light	Light sources that affect the coloring of patch and surface objects
Line	Line used by functions such as `plot`, `plot3`, `semilogx`
Patch	Filled polygon with edges
Rectangle	Two-dimensional shape varying from rectangles to ovals
Surface	Three-dimensional representation of matrix data created by plotting the value of the data as heights above the x-y plane
Text	Character string

Object Hierarchy

The objects are organized in a tree structured hierarchy reflecting their interdependence. For example, line objects require axes objects as a frame of reference. In turn, axes objects exist only within figure objects. This diagram illustrates the tree structure.

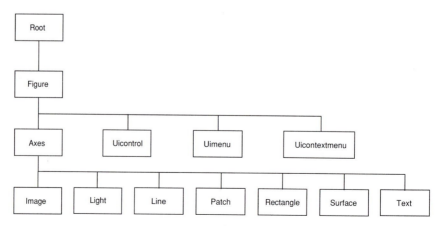

Creating Objects

Each object has an associated function that creates the object. These functions have the same name as the objects they create. For example, the text function creates text objects, the figure function creates figure objects, and so on. MATLAB's high-level graphics functions (like plot and surf) call the appropriate low-level function to draw their respective graphics.

For More Information See the object creation function reference page for more information about the object and a description of the object's properties.

Commands for Working with Objects

This table lists commands commonly used when working with objects.

Function	Purpose
copyobj	Copy graphics object
delete	Delete an object
findobj	Find the handle of objects having specified property values
gca	Return the handle of the current axes
gcf	Return the handle of the current figure
gco	Return the handle of the current object
get	Query the value of an objects properties
set	Set the value of an objects properties

For More Information See MATLAB Functions in the Help Desk for a description of each of these functions.

Setting Object Properties

All object properties have default values. However, you may find it useful to change the settings of some properties to customize your graph. There are two ways to set object properties:

- Specify values for properties when you create the object.
- Set the property value on an object that already exists.

You can specify object property values as arguments to object creation functions as well as with plotting function, such as plot, mesh, and surf. You can use the set command to modify the property values of existing objects.

For More Information See Handle Graphics Properties in the Help Desk for a description of all object properties.

Setting Properties from Plotting Commands

Plotting commands that create lines or surfaces enable you to specify property name/property value pairs as arguments. For example, the command

```
plot(x,y,'LineWidth',1.5)
```

plots the data in the variables x and y using lines having a LineWidth property set to 1.5 points (one point = 1/72 inch). You can set any line object property this way.

Setting Properties of Existing Objects

Many plotting commands can also return the handles of the objects created so you can modify the objects using the set command. For example, these statements plot a five-by-five matrix (creating five lines, one per column) and then set the Marker to a square and the MarkerFaceColor to green.

```
h = plot(magic(5));
set(h,'Marker','s',MarkerFaceColor','g')
```

In this case, h is a vector containing five handles, one for each of the five lines in the plot. The set statement sets the Marker and MarkerFaceColor properties of all lines to the same values.

Setting Multiple Property Values

If you want to set the properties of each line to a different value, you can use cell arrays to store all the data and pass it to the set command. For example, create a plot and save the line handles.

```
h = plot(magic(5));
```

Suppose you want to add different markers to each line and color the marker's face color to the same color as the line. You need to define two cell arrays – one containing the property names and the other containing the desired values of the properties.

The prop_name cell array contains two elements.

```
prop_name(1) = {'Marker'};
prop_name(2) = {'MarkerFaceColor'};
```

The prop_values cell array contains 10 values – five values for the Marker property and five values for the MarkerFaceColor property. Notice that prop_values is a two-dimensional cell array. The first dimension indicates which handle in h the values apply to and the second dimension indicates which property the value is assigned to.

```
prop_values(1,1) = {'s'};
prop_values(1,2) = {get(h(1),'Color')};
prop_values(2,1) = {'d'};
prop_values(2,2) = {get(h(2),'Color')};
prop_values(3,1) = {'o'};
prop_values(3,2) = {get(h(3),'Color')};
prop_values(4,1) = {'p'};
prop_values(4,2) = {get(h(4),'Color')};
prop_values(5,1) = {'h'};
prop_values(5,2) = {get(h(5),'Color')};
```

The MarkerFaceColor is always assigned the value of the corresponding line's color (obtained by getting the line's Color property with the get command).

After defining the cell arrays, call set to specify the new property values.

```
set(h,prop_name,prop_values)
```

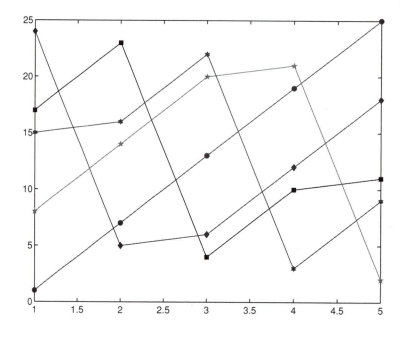

For More Information See the "Structures and Cell Arrays" chapter in *Using MATLAB* for information on cell arrays. Access *Using MATLAB* from the Help Desk.

Finding the Handles of Existing Objects

The findobj command enables you to obtain the handles of graphics objects by searching for objects with particular property values. With findobj you can specify the value of any combination of properties, which makes it easy to pick one object out of many. For example, you may want to find the blue line with square marker having blue face color.

You can also specify which figures or axes to search, if there is more than one. The following sections provide examples illustrating how to use findobj.

Finding All Objects of a Certain Type

Since all objects have a Type property that identifies the type of object, you can find the handles of all occurrences of a particular type of object. For example,

```
h = findobj('Type','line');
```

finds the handles of all line objects.

Finding Objects with a Particular Property

You can specify multiple properties to narrow the search. For example,

```
h = findobj('Type','line','Color','r','LineStyle',':');
```

finds the handles of all red, dotted lines.

Limiting the Scope of the Search

You can specify the starting point in the object hierarchy by passing the handle of the starting figure or axes as the first argument. For example,

```
h = findobj(gca,'Type','text','String','\pi/2');
```

finds the string π/2 only within the current axes.

Using findobj as an Argument

Since findobj returns the handles it finds, you can use it in place of the handle argument. For example,

```
set(findobj('Type','line','Color','red'),'LineStyle',':')
```

finds all red lines and sets their line style to dotted.

For More Information See the "Accessing Object Handles" section of the Handle Graphics chapter in *Using MATLAB Graphics* for more information. Access *Using MATLAB Graphics* from the Help Desk.

Graphics User Interfaces

Here is a simple example illustrating how to use Handle Graphics to build user interfaces. The statement

```
b = uicontrol('Style','pushbutton', ...
      'Units','normalized', ...
      'Position',[.5 .5 .2 .1], ...
      'String','click here');
```

creates a pushbutton in the center of a figure window and returns a handle to the new object. But, so far, clicking on the button does nothing. The statement

```
s = 'set(b,''Position'',[.8*rand .9*rand .2 .1])';
```

creates a string containing a command that alters the pushbutton's position. Repeated execution of

```
eval(s)
```

moves the button to random positions. Finally,

```
set(b,'Callback',s)
```

installs s as the button's callback action, so every time you click on the button, it moves to a new position.

Graphical User Interface Design Tools

MATLAB provides GUI Design Environment (GUIDE) tools that simplify the creation of graphical user interfaces. To display the GUIDE control panel, issue the guide command.

For More Information Type help guide at the MATLAB command line.

Animations

MATLAB provides two ways of generating moving, animated graphics:

- Continually erase and then redraw the objects on the screen, making incremental changes with each redraw.
- Save a number of different pictures and then play them back as a movie.

Erase Mode Method

Using the EraseMode property is appropriate for long sequences of simple plots where the change from frame to frame is minimal. Here is an example showing simulated Brownian motion. Specify a number of points, such as

```
n = 20
```

and a temperature or velocity, such as

```
s = .02
```

The best values for these two parameters depend upon the speed of your particular computer. Generate n random points with (x,y) coordinates between $-1/2$ and $+1/2$.

```
x = rand(n,1)-0.5;
y = rand(n,1)-0.5;
```

Plot the points in a square with sides at -1 and +1. Save the handle for the vector of points and set its EraseMode to xor. This tells the MATLAB graphics system not to redraw the entire plot when the coordinates of one point are changed, but to restore the background color in the vicinity of the point using an "exclusive or" operation.

```
h = plot(x,y,'.');
axis([-1 1 -1 1])
axis square
grid off
set(h,'EraseMode','xor','MarkerSize',18)
```

Now begin the animation. Here is an infinite while loop, which you can eventually exit by typing **Ctrl-c**. Each time through the loop, add a small amount of normally distributed random noise to the coordinates of the points.

Then, instead of creating an entirely new plot, simply change the XData and YData properties of the original plot.

```
while 1
   drawnow
   x = x + s*randn(n,1);
   y = y + s*randn(n,1);
   set(h,'XData',x,'YData',y)
end
```

How long does it take for one of the points to get outside of the square? How long before all of the points are outside the square?

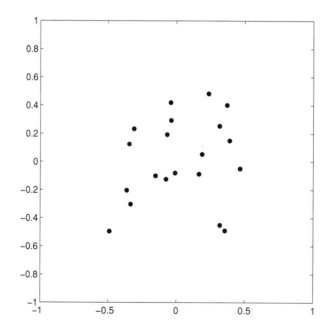

Creating Movies

If you increase the number of points in the Brownian motion example to something like n = 300 and s = .02, the motion is no longer very fluid; it takes too much time to draw each time step. It becomes more effective to save a predetermined number of frames as bitmaps and to play them back as a *movie*.

First, decide on the number of frames, say

```
nframes = 50;
```

Next, set up the first plot as before, except using the default EraseMode (normal).

```
x = rand(n,1)-0.5;
y = rand(n,1)-0.5;
h = plot(x,y,'.');
set(h,'MarkerSize',18);
axis([-1 1 -1 1])
axis square
grid off
```

Generate the movie and use getframe to capture each frame.

```
for k = 1:nframes
   x = x + s*randn(n,1);
   y = y + s*randn(n,1);
   set(h,'XData',x,'YData',y)
   M(k) = getframe;
end
```

Finally, play the movie 30 times.

```
movie(M,30)
```

5

Programming
with MATLAB

Flow Control

MATLAB has several flow control constructs:

- if statements
- switch statements
- for loops
- while loops
- break statements

For More Information *Using MATLAB* discusses programming in MATLAB. Access *Using MATLAB* from the Help Desk.

---

if

The if statement evaluates a logical expression and executes a group of statements when the expression is *true*. The optional elseif and else keywords provide for the execution of alternate groups of statements. An end keyword, which matches the if, terminates the last group of statements. The groups of statements are delineated by the four keywords – no braces or brackets are involved.

MATLAB's algorithm for generating a magic square of order n involves three different cases: when n is odd, when n is even but not divisible by 4, or when n is divisible by 4. This is described by

```
if rem(n,2) ~= 0
   M = odd_magic(n)
elseif rem(n,4) ~= 0
   M = single_even_magic(n)
else
   M = double_even_magic(n)
end
```

In this example, the three cases are mutually exclusive, but if they weren't, the first *true* condition would be executed.

It is important to understand how relational operators and if statements work with matrices. When you want to check for equality between two variables, you might use

```
if A == B, ...
```

This is legal MATLAB code, and does what you expect when A and B are scalars. But when A and B are matrices, A == B does not test *if* they are equal, it tests *where* they are equal; the result is another matrix of 0's and 1's showing element-by-element equality. In fact, if A and B are not the same size, then A == B is an error.

The proper way to check for equality between two variables is to use the isequal function,

```
if isequal(A,B), ...
```

Here is another example to emphasize this point. If A and B are scalars, the following program will never reach the unexpected situation. But for most pairs of matrices, including our magic squares with interchanged columns, none of the matrix conditions A > B, A < B or A == B is true for *all* elements and so the else clause is executed.

```
if A > B
    'greater'
elseif A < B
    'less'
elseif A == B
    'equal'
else
    error('Unexpected situation')
end
```

Several functions are helpful for reducing the results of matrix comparisons to scalar conditions for use with if, including

```
isequal
isempty
all
any
```

switch and case

The switch statement executes groups of statements based on the value of a variable or expression. The keywords case and otherwise delineate the groups. Only the first matching case is executed. There must always be an end to match the switch.

The logic of the magic squares algorithm can also be described by

```
switch (rem(n,4)==0) + (rem(n,2)==0)
   case 0
      M = odd_magic(n)
   case 1
      M = single_even_magic(n)
   case 2
      M = double_even_magic(n)
   otherwise
      error('This is impossible')
end
```

Note for C Programmers Unlike the C language switch statement, MATLAB's switch does not fall through. If the first case statement is *true*, the other case statements do not execute. So, break statements are not required.

---

for

The for loop repeats a group of statements a fixed, predetermined number of times. A matching end delineates the statements.

```
for n = 3:32
   r(n) = rank(magic(n));
end
r
```

The semicolon terminating the inner statement suppresses repeated printing, and the r after the loop displays the final result.

It is a good idea to indent the loops for readability, especially when they are nested.

```
for i = 1:m
    for j = 1:n
        H(i,j) = 1/(i+j);
    end
end
```

while

The while loop repeats a group of statements an indefinite number of times under control of a logical condition. A matching end delineates the statements.

Here is a complete program, illustrating while, if, else, and end, that uses interval bisection to find a zero of a polynomial.

```
a = 0; fa = -Inf;
b = 3; fb = Inf;
while b-a > eps*b
    x = (a+b)/2;
    fx = x^3-2*x-5;
    if sign(fx) == sign(fa)
        a = x; fa = fx;
    else
        b = x; fb = fx;
    end
end
x
```

The result is a root of the polynomial $x^3 - 2x - 5$, namely

```
x =
    2.09455148154233
```

The cautions involving matrix comparisons that are discussed in the section on the if statement also apply to the while statement.

break

The break statement lets you exit early from a for or while loop. In nested loops, break exits from the innermost loop only.

Here is an improvement on the example from the previous section. Why is this use of break a good idea?

```
a = 0;  fa = -Inf;
b = 3;  fb = Inf;
while b-a > eps*b
   x = (a+b)/2;
   fx = x^3-2*x-5;
   if fx == 0
      break
   elseif sign(fx) == sign(fa)
      a = x;  fa = fx;
   else
      b = x;  fb = fx;
   end
end
x
```

Other Data Structures

This section introduces you to some other data structures in MATLAB, including:

- Multidimensional arrays
- Cell arrays
- Characters and text
- Structures

For More Information For a complete discussion of MATLAB's data structures, see *Using MATLAB*, which is accessible from the Help Desk.

Multidimensional Arrays

Multidimensional arrays in MATLAB are arrays with more than two subscripts. They can be created by calling zeros, ones, rand, or randn with more than two arguments. For example,

```
R = randn(3,4,5);
```

creates a 3-by-4-by-5 array with a total of 3x4x5 = 60 normally distributed random elements.

A three-dimensional array might represent three-dimensional physical data, say the temperature in a room, sampled on a rectangular grid. Or, it might represent a sequence of matrices, $A^{(k)}$, or samples of a time-dependent matrix, $A(t)$. In these latter cases, the (i, j)th element of the kth matrix, or the t_kth matrix, is denoted by A(i,j,k).

MATLAB's and Dürer's versions of the magic square of order 4 differ by an interchange of two columns. Many different magic squares can be generated by interchanging columns. The statement

```
p = perms(1:4);
```

generates the 4! = 24 permutations of 1:4. The kth permutation is the row vector, p(k,:). Then

```
A = magic(4);
M = zeros(4,4,24);
for k = 1:24
    M(:,:,k) = A(:,p(k,:));
end
```

stores the sequence of 24 magic squares in a three-dimensional array, M. The size of M is

```
size(M)
```

```
ans =
     4     4    24
```

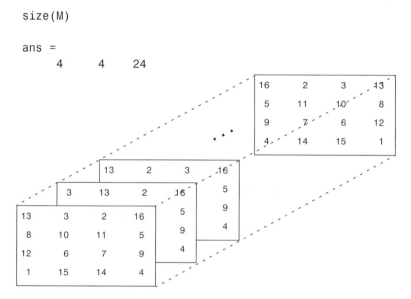

It turns out that the 22nd matrix in the sequence is Dürer's:

```
M(:,:,22)
```

```
ans =
    16     3     2    13
     5    10    11     8
     9     6     7    12
     4    15    14     1
```

The statement

```
sum(M,d)
```

computes sums by varying the dth subscript. So

```
sum(M,1)
```

is a 1-by-4-by-24 array containing 24 copies of the row vector

```
34      34      34      34
```

and

```
sum(M,2)
```

is a 4-by-1-by-24 array containing 24 copies of the column vector

```
34
34
34
34
```

Finally,

```
S = sum(M,3)
```

adds the 24 matrices in the sequence. The result has size 4-by-4-by-1, so it looks like a 4-by-4 array,

```
S =
    204     204     204     204
    204     204     204     204
    204     204     204     204
    204     204     204     204
```

Cell Arrays

Cell arrays in MATLAB are multidimensional arrays whose elements are copies of other arrays. A cell array of empty matrices can be created with the cell function. But, more often, cell arrays are created by enclosing a miscellaneous collection of things in curly braces, {}. The curly braces are also used with subscripts to access the contents of various cells. For example,

```
C = {A sum(A) prod(prod(A))}
```

produces a 1-by-3 cell array. The three cells contain the magic square, the row vector of column sums, and the product of all its elements. When C is displayed, you see

```
C =
    [4x4 double]    [1x4 double]    [20922789888000]
```

This is because the first two cells are too large to print in this limited space, but the third cell contains only a single number, 16!, so there is room to print it.

Here are two important points to remember. First, to retrieve the contents of one of the cells, use subscripts in curly braces. For example, C{1} retrieves the magic square and C{3} is 16!. Second, cell arrays contain *copies* of other arrays, not *pointers* to those arrays. If you subsequently change A, nothing happens to C.

Three-dimensional arrays can be used to store a sequence of matrices of the *same* size. Cell arrays can be used to store a sequence of matrices of *different* sizes. For example,

```
M = cell(8,1);
for n = 1:8
   M{n} = magic(n);
end
M
```

produces a sequence of magic squares of different order,

```
M =
    [            1]
    [ 2x2  double]
    [ 3x3  double]
    [ 4x4  double]
    [ 5x5  double]
    [ 6x6  double]
    [ 7x7  double]
    [ 8x8  double]
```

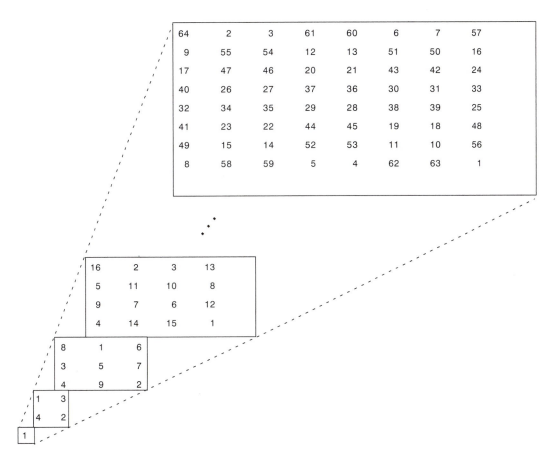

You can retrieve our old friend with

```
M{4}
```

Characters and Text

Enter text into MATLAB using single quotes. For example,

```
s = 'Hello'
```

The result is not the same kind of numeric matrix or array we have been dealing with up to now. It is a 1-by-5 character array.

Internally, the characters are stored as numbers, but not in floating-point format. The statement

```
a = double(s)
```

converts the character array to a numeric matrix containing floating-point representations of the ASCII codes for each character. The result is

```
a =
    72   101   108   108   111
```

The statement

```
s = char(a)
```

reverses the conversion.

Converting numbers to characters makes it possible to investigate the various fonts available on your computer. The printable characters in the basic ASCII character set are represented by the integers 32:127. (The integers less than 32 represent nonprintable control characters.) These integers are arranged in an appropriate 6-by-16 array with

```
F = reshape(32:127,16,6)';
```

The printable characters in the extended ASCII character set are represented by F+128. When these integers are interpreted as characters, the result depends on the font currently being used. Type the statements

```
char(F)
char(F+128)
```

and then vary the font being used for the MATLAB command window. On a PC, select **Preferences** under the **File** menu. Be sure to try the **Symbol** and

Wingdings fonts, if you have them on your computer. Here is one example of the kind of output you might obtain.

```
 !"#$%&'()*+,-./
0123456789:;<=>?
@ABCDEFGHIJKLMNO
PQRSTUVWXYZ[\]^_
`abcdefghijklmno
pqrstuvwxyz{|}~-

†°¢£§·¶ß®©™´¨¦ÆØ
×±ðŠ¥µ123¼½ªº¾æø
¿¡¬ÐƒÝý«»…þÀÃÕŒœ
-—""''÷ÞÿŸ/¤‹›??
‡·,„‰ÂÊÁËÈÍÎÏÌÓÔ
šÒÚÛÙ`ˆ˜¯`Ž°¸"žÿ
```

Concatenation with square brackets joins text variables together into larger strings. The statement

```
h = [s, ' world']
```

joins the strings horizontally and produces

```
h =
    Hello world
```

The statement

```
v = [s; 'world']
```

joins the strings vertically and produces

```
v =
    Hello
    world
```

Note that a blank has to be inserted before the `'w'` in h and that both words in v have to have the same length. The resulting arrays are both character arrays; h is 1-by-11 and v is 2-by-5.

To manipulate a body of text containing lines of different lengths, you have two choices – a padded character array or a cell array of strings. The char function accepts any number of lines, adds blanks to each line to make them all the same length, and forms a character array with each line in a separate row. For example,

```
S = char('A','rolling','stone','gathers','momentum.')
```

produces a 5-by-9 character array

```
S =
A
rolling
stone
gathers
momentum.
```

There are enough blanks in each of the first four rows of S to make all the rows the same length. Alternatively, you can store the text in a cell array. For example,

```
C = {'A';'rolling';'stone';'gathers';'momentum.'}
```

is a 5-by-1 cell array

```
C =
    'A'
    'rolling'
    'stone'
    'gathers'
    'momentum.'
```

You can convert a padded character array to a cell array of strings with

```
C = cellstr(S)
```

and reverse the process with

```
S = char(C)
```

Structures

Structures are multidimensional MATLAB arrays with elements accessed by textual *field designators*. For example,

```
S.name = 'Ed Plum';
S.score = 83;
S.grade = 'B+'
```

creates a scalar structure with three fields.

```
S =
     name: 'Ed Plum'
    score: 83
    grade: 'B+'
```

Like everything else in MATLAB, structures are arrays, so you can insert additional elements. In this case, each element of the array is a structure with several fields. The fields can be added one at a time,

```
S(2).name = 'Toni Miller';
S(2).score = 91;
S(2).grade = 'A-';
```

or, an entire element can be added with a single statement.

```
S(3) = struct('name','Jerry Garcia',...
              'score',70,'grade','C')
```

Now the structure is large enough that only a summary is printed.

```
S =
1x3 struct array with fields:
    name
    score
    grade
```

There are several ways to reassemble the various fields into other MATLAB arrays. They are all based on the notation of a *comma separated list*. If you type

```
S.score
```

it is the same as typing

```
S(1).score, S(2).score, S(3).score
```

This is a comma separated list. Without any other punctuation, it is not very useful. It assigns the three scores, one at a time, to the default variable ans and dutifully prints out the result of each assignment. But when you enclose the expression in square brackets,

```
[S.score]
```

it is the same as

```
[S(1).score, S(2).score, S(3).score]
```

which produces a numeric row vector containing all of the scores.

```
ans =
    83    91    70
```

Similarly, typing

```
S.name
```

just assigns the names, one at time, to ans. But enclosing the expression in curly braces,

```
{S.name}
```

creates a 1-by-3 cell array containing the three names.

```
ans =
    'Ed Plum'    'Toni Miller'    'Jerry Garcia'
```

And

```
char(S.name)
```

calls the char function with three arguments to create a character array from the name fields,

```
ans =
Ed Plum
Toni Miller
Jerry Garcia
```

Scripts and Functions

MATLAB is a powerful programming language as well as an interactive computational environment. Files that contain code in the MATLAB language are called M-files. You create M-files using a text editor, then use them as you would any other MATLAB function or command.

There are two kinds of M-files:

- Scripts, which do not accept input arguments or return output arguments. They operate on data in the workspace.
- Functions, which can accept input arguments and return output arguments. Internal variables are local to the function.

If you're a new MATLAB programmer, just create the M-files that you want to try out in the current directory. As you develop more of your own M-files, you will want to organize them into other directories and personal toolboxes that you can add to MATLAB's search path.

If you duplicate function names, MATLAB executes the one that occurs first in the search path.

To view the contents of an M-file, for example, `myfunction.m`, use

```
type myfunction
```

Scripts

When you invoke a *script*, MATLAB simply executes the commands found in the file. Scripts can operate on existing data in the workspace, or they can create new data on which to operate. Although scripts do not return output arguments, any variables that they create remain in the workspace, to be used in subsequent computations. In addition, scripts can produce graphical output using functions like `plot`.

For example, create a file called `magicrank.m` that contains these MATLAB commands.

```
% Investigate the rank of magic squares
r = zeros(1,32);
for n = 3:32
   r(n) = rank(magic(n));
end
r
bar(r)
```

Typing the statement

```
magicrank
```

causes MATLAB to execute the commands, compute the rank of the first 30 magic squares, and plot a bar graph of the result. After execution of the file is complete, the variables n and r remain in the workspace.

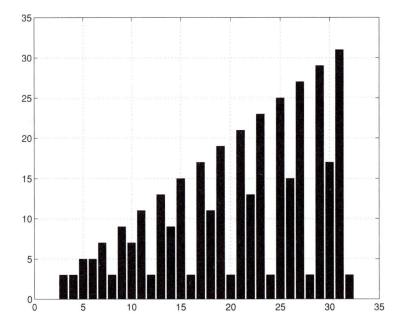

Functions

Functions are M-files that can accept input arguments and return output arguments. The name of the M-file and of the function should be the same. Functions operate on variables within their own workspace, separate from the workspace you access at the MATLAB command prompt.

A good example is provided by rank. The M-file rank.m is available in the directory

```
toolbox/matlab/matfun
```

You can see the file with

```
type rank
```

Here is the file.

```
function r = rank(A,tol)
%   RANK Matrix rank.
%   RANK(A) provides an estimate of the number of linearly
%   independent rows or columns of a matrix A.
%   RANK(A,tol) is the number of singular values of A
%   that are larger than tol.
%   RANK(A) uses the default tol = max(size(A)) * norm(A) * eps.

s = svd(A);
if nargin==1
   tol = max(size(A)') * max(s) * eps;
end
r = sum(s > tol);
```

The first line of a function M-file starts with the keyword function. It gives the function name and order of arguments. In this case, there are up to two input arguments and one output argument.

The next several lines, up to the first blank or executable line, are comment lines that provide the help text. These lines are printed when you type

```
help rank
```

The first line of the help text is the H1 line, which MATLAB displays when you use the lookfor command or request help on a directory.

The rest of the file is the executable MATLAB code defining the function. The variable s introduced in the body of the function, as well as the variables on the first line, r, A and tol, are all *local* to the function; they are separate from any variables in the MATLAB workspace.

This example illustrates one aspect of MATLAB functions that is not ordinarily found in other programming languages – a variable number of arguments. The rank function can be used in several different ways.

```
rank(A)
r = rank(A)
r = rank(A,1.e-6)
```

Many M-files work this way. If no output argument is supplied, the result is stored in ans. If the second input argument is not supplied, the function computes a default value. Within the body of the function, two quantities named nargin and nargout are available which tell you the number of input and output arguments involved in each particular use of the function. The rank function uses nargin, but does not need to use nargout.

Global Variables

If you want more than one function to share a single copy of a variable, simply declare the variable as global in all the functions. Do the same thing at the command line if you want the base workspace to access the variable. The global declaration must occur before the variable is actually used in a function. Although it is not required, using capital letters for the names of global variables helps distinguish them from other variables. For example, create an M-file called falling.m.

```
function h = falling(t)
global GRAVITY
h = 1/2*GRAVITY*t.^2;
```

Then interactively enter the statements

```
global GRAVITY
GRAVITY = 32;
y = falling((0:.1:5)');
```

The two global statements make the value assigned to GRAVITY at the command prompt available inside the function. You can then modify GRAVITY interactively and obtain new solutions without editing any files.

Passing String Arguments to Functions

You can write MATLAB functions that accept string arguments without the parentheses and quotes. That is, MATLAB interprets

```
foo a b c
```

as

```
foo('a','b','c')
```

However, when using the unquoted form, MATLAB cannot return output arguments. For example,

```
legend apples oranges
```

creates a legend on a plot using the strings apples and oranges as labels. If you want the legend command to return its output arguments, then you must use the quoted form.

```
[legh,objh] = legend('apples','oranges');
```

In addition, you cannot use the unquoted form if any of the arguments are not strings.

Building Strings on the Fly

The quoted form enables you to construct string arguments within the code. The following example processes multiple data files, August1.dat, August2.dat, and so on. It uses the function int2str, which converts an integer to a character, to build the filename.

```
for d = 1:31
    s = ['August' int2str(d) '.dat'];
    load(s)
    % Code to process the contents of the d-th file
end
```

A Cautionary Note

While the unquoted syntax is convenient, it can be used incorrectly without causing MATLAB to generate an error. For example, given a matrix A,

```
A =
        0    -6    -1
        6     2   -16
       -5    20   -10
```

The eig command returns the eigenvalues of A.

```
eig(A)
ans =
  -3.0710
  -2.4645+17.6008i
  -2.4645-17.6008i
```

The following statement is not allowed because A is not a string, however MATLAB does not generate an error.

```
eig A
ans =
    65
```

MATLAB actually takes the eigenvalues of ASCII numeric equivalent of the letter A (which is the number 65).

The eval Function

The eval function works with text variables to implement a powerful text macro facility. The expression or statement

```
eval(s)
```

uses the MATLAB interpreter to evaluate the expression or execute the statement contained in the text string s.

The example of the previous section could also be done with the following code, although this would be somewhat less efficient because it involves the full interpreter, not just a function call.

```
for d = 1:31
    s = ['load August' int2str(d) '.dat'];
    eval(s)
    % Process the contents of the d-th file
end
```

Vectorization

To obtain the most speed out of MATLAB, it's important to vectorize the algorithms in your M-files. Where other programming languages might use for or DO loops, MATLAB can use vector or matrix operations. A simple example involves creating a table of logarithms.

```
x = 0;
for k = 1:1001
    y(k) = log10(x);
    x = x + .01;
end
```

Experienced MATLAB users like to say "Life is too short to spend writing for loops."

A vectorized version of the same code is

```
x = 0:.01:10;
y = log10(x);
```

For more complicated code, vectorization options are not always so obvious. When speed is important, however, you should always look for ways to vectorize your algorithms.

Preallocation

If you can't vectorize a piece of code, you can make your for loops go faster by preallocating any vectors or arrays in which output results are stored. For example, this code uses the function zeros to preallocate the vector created in the for loop. This makes the for loop execute significantly faster.

```
r = zeros(32,1);
for n = 1:32
    r(n) = rank(magic(n));
end
```

Without the preallocation in the previous example, the MATLAB interpreter enlarges the r vector by one element each time through the loop. Vector preallocation eliminates this step and results in faster execution.

Function Functions

A class of functions, called "function functions," works with nonlinear functions of a scalar variable. That is, one function works on another function. The function functions include:

- Zero finding
- Optimization
- Quadrature
- Ordinary differential equations

MATLAB represents the nonlinear function by a function M-file. For example, here is a simplified version of the function humps from the matlab/demos directory.

```
function y = humps(x)
y = 1./((x-.3).^2 + .01) + 1./((x-.9).^2 + .04) - 6;
```

Evaluate this function at a set of points in the interval $0 \le x \le 1$ with

```
x = 0:.002:1;
y = humps(x);
```

Then plot the function with

```
plot(x,y)
```

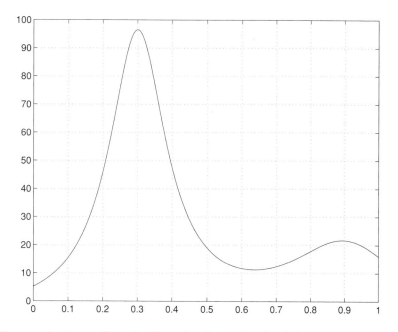

The graph shows that the function has a local minimum near $x = 0.6$. The function fmins finds the *minimizer*, the value of x where the function takes on this minimum. The first argument to fmins is the name of the function being minimized and the second argument is a rough guess at the location of the minimum.

```
p = fmins('humps',.5)
p =
    0.6370
```

To evaluate the function at the minimizer,

```
humps(p)

ans =
    11.2528
```

Numerical analysts use the terms *quadrature* and *integration* to distinguish between numerical approximation of definite integrals and numerical integration of ordinary differential equations. MATLAB's quadrature routines are quad and quad8. The statement

```
Q = quad8('humps',0,1)
```

computes the area under the curve in the graph and produces

```
Q =
   29.8583
```

Finally, the graph shows that the function is never zero on this interval. So, if you search for a zero with

```
z = fzero('humps',.5)
```

you will find one outside of the interval

```
z =
   -0.1316
```

Demonstration Programs Included with MATLAB

This section includes information on many of the demonstration programs that are included with MATLAB.

For More Information The MathWorks Web site (www.mathworks.com) contains numerous M-files that have been written by users and MathWorks staff. These are accessible by selecting **Download M-Files**. Also, Technical Notes, which is accessible from our Technical Support Web site (www.mathworks.com/support), contains numerous examples on graphics, mathematics, API, Simulink, and others.

There are many programs included with MATLAB that highlight various features and functions. For a complete list of the demos, at the command prompt type

```
help demos
```

To view a specific file, for example, airfoil, type

```
edit airfoil
```

To run a demonstration, type the filename at the command prompt. For example, to run the airfoil demonstration, type

```
airfoil
```

Note Many of the demonstrations use multiple windows and require you to press a key in the MATLAB command window to continue through the demonstration.

These are the current demonstration programs.

Table 5-1: MATLAB Demonstration Programs

Matrices	
airfoil	Graphical demonstration of sparse matrix from NASA airfoil.
buckydem	Connectivity graph of the Buckminster Fuller geodesic dome.
delsqdemo	Finite difference Laplacian on various domains.
eigmovie	Symmetric eigenvalue movie.
eigshow	Graphical demonstration of matrix eigenvalues.
intro	Introduction to basic matrix operations in MATLAB.
inverter	Demonstration of the inversion of a large matrix.
matmanip	Introduction to matrix manipulation.
rrefmovie	Computation of reduced row echelon form.
sepdemo	Separators for a finite element mesh.
sparsity	Demonstration of the effect of sparsity orderings.
svdshow	Graphical demonstration of matrix singular values.
Numerics	
bench	MATLAB benchmark.
census	Prediction of the U.S. population in the year 2000.
e2pi	Two-dimensional, visual solution to the problem "Which is greater, e^{π} or π^{e}?"
fftdemo	Use of the FFT function for spectral analysis.
fitdemo	Nonlinear curve fit with simplex algorithm.
fplotdemo	Demonstration of plotting a function.

Table 5-1: MATLAB Demonstration Programs (Continued)

funfuns	Demonstration of functions operating on other functions.
lotkademo	Example of ordinary differential equation solution.
quaddemo	Adaptive quadrature.
quake	Loma Prieta earthquake.
spline2d	Demonstration of ginput and spline in two dimensions.
sunspots	Demonstration of the fast Fourier transform (FFT) function in MATLAB used to analyze the variations in sunspot activity.
zerodemo	Zero finding with fzero.
Visualization	
colormenu	Demonstration of adding a colormap to the current figure.
cplxdemo	Maps of functions of a complex variable.
earthmap	Graphical demonstrations of earth's topography.
graf2d	Two-dimensional XY plots in MATLAB.
graf2d2	Three-dimensional XYZ plots in MATLAB.
grafcplx	Demonstration of complex function plots in MATLAB.
imagedemo	Demonstration of MATLAB's image capability.
imageext	Demonstration of changing and rotating image colormaps.
lorenz	Graphical demonstration of the orbit around the Lorenz chaotic attractor.
penny	Several views of the penny data.
vibes	Vibrating L-shaped membrane movie.

Table 5-1: MATLAB Demonstration Programs (Continued)

xfourier	Graphical demonstration of Fourier series expansion.
xpklein	Klein bottle demo.
xpsound	Demonstration of MATLAB's sound capability.
Language	
graf3d	Demonstration of Handle Graphics for surface plots.
hndlaxis	Demonstration of Handle Graphics for axes.
hndlgraf	Demonstration of Handle Graphics for line plots.
xplang	Introduction to the MATLAB language.
ODE Suite	
a2ode	Stiff problem, linear with real eigenvalues.
a3ode	Stiff problem, linear with real eigenvalues.
b5ode	Stiff problem, linear with complex eigenvalues.
ballode	Equations of motion for a bouncing ball used by BALLDEMO.
besslode	Bessel's equation of order 0 used by BESSLDEMO.
brussode	Stiff problem, modelling a chemical reaction (Brusselator).
buiode	Stiff problem, analytical solution due to Bui.
chm6ode	Stiff problem CHM6 from Enright and Hull.
chm7ode	Stiff problem CHM7 from Enright and Hull.
chm9ode	Stiff problem CHM9 from Enright and Hull.
d1ode	Stiff problem, nonlinear with real eigenvalues.
fem1ode	Stiff problem with a time-dependent mass matrix.
fem2ode	Stiff problem with a time-independent mass matrix.

Table 5-1: MATLAB Demonstration Programs (Continued)

gearode	Stiff problem due to Gear as quoted by van der Houwen.
hb1ode	Stiff problem 1 of Hindmarsh and Byrne.
hb2ode	Stiff problem 2 of Hindmarsh and Byrne.
hb3ode	Stiff problem 3 of Hindmarsh and Byrne.
odedemo	Demonstration of the ODE suite integrators.
orbitode	Restricted 3 body problem used by ORBITDEMO.
orbt2ode	Nonstiff problem D5 of Hull et al.
rigidode	Euler equations of a rigid body without external forces.
sticode	Spring-driven mass stuck to surface, used by STICDEMO.
vdpode	Parameterizable van der Pol equation (stiff for large μ).
Gallery	
cruller	Graphical demonstration of a cruller.
klein1	Graphical demonstration of a Klein bottle.
knot	Tube surrounding a three-dimensional knot.
logo	Graphical demonstration of the MATLAB L-shaped membrane logo.
modes	Graphical demonstration of 12 modes of the L-shaped membrane.
quivdemo	Graphical demonstration of the quiver function.
spharm2	Graphical demonstration of spherical surface harmonic.
tori4	Graphical demonstration of four-linked, unknotted tori.

Table 5-1: MATLAB Demonstration Programs (Continued)

Games

bblwrap	Bubblewrap.
life	Conway's Game of Life.
soma	Soma cube.
xpbombs	Minesweeper game.

Miscellaneous

codec	Alphabet transposition coder/decoder.
crulspin	Spinning cruller movie.
logospin	Movie of the MathWorks logo spinning.
makevase	Demonstration of a surface of revolution.
quatdemo	Quaternion rotation.
spinner	Colorful lines spinning through space.
travel	Traveling salesman problem.
truss	Animation of a bending bridge truss.
wrldtrv	Great circle flight routes around the globe.
xphide	Visual perception of objects in motion.
xpquad	Superquadrics plotting demonstration.

Helper Functions

bucky	Graph of the Buckminster Fuller geodesic dome.
cmdlnbgn	Set up for command line demos.
cmdlnend	Clean up after command line demos.
cmdlnwin	Demo gateway routine for running command line demos.

Table 5-1: MATLAB Demonstration Programs (Continued)

finddemo	Command that finds available demos for individual toolboxes.
helpfun	Utility function for displaying help text conveniently.
membrane	The MathWorks logo.
peaks	Sample function of two variables.
pltmat	Command that displays a matrix in a figure window.

6

Symbolic Math Toolbox

Introduction

The Symbolic Math Toolbox incorporates symbolic computation into MATLAB's numeric environment. This toolbox supplements MATLAB's numeric and graphical facilities with several other types of mathematical computation.

Facility	Covers
Calculus	Differentiation, integration, limits, summation, and Taylor series
Linear Algebra	Inverses, determinants, eigenvalues, singular value decomposition, and canonical forms of symbolic matrices
Simplification	Methods of simplifying algebraic expressions
Solution of Equations	Symbolic and numerical solutions to algebraic and differential equations
Transforms	Fourier, Laplace, z-transform, and corresponding inverse transforms
Variable-Precision Arithmetic	Numerical evaluation of mathematical expressions to any specified accuracy

The computational engine underlying the toolboxes is the kernel of Maple, a system developed primarily at the University of Waterloo, Canada, and, more recently, at the Eidgenössiche Technische Hochschule, Zürich, Switzerland. Maple is marketed and supported by Waterloo Maple, Inc.

This version of the Symbolic Math Toolbox is designed to work with MATLAB 5.3 and Maple V Release 5.

The Symbolic Math Toolbox is a collection of more than one-hundred MATLAB functions that provide access to the Maple kernel using a syntax and style that is a natural extension of the MATLAB language. The toolbox also allows you to access functions in Maple's linear algebra package. With this toolbox, you can write your own M-files to access Maple functions and the Maple workspace.

The following sections of this tutorial provide explanation and examples on how to use the toolbox.

Section	Covers
"Getting Help"	How to get online help for Symbolic Math Toolbox functions
"Getting Started"	Basic symbolic math operations
"Calculus"	How to differentiate and integrate symbolic expressions
"Simplifications and Substitutions"	How to simplify and substitute values into expressions
"Variable-Precision Arithmetic"	How to control the precision of computations
"Linear Algebra"	Examples using the toolbox functions
"Solving Equations"	How to solve symbolic equations

For More Information You can access complete reference information for the Symbolic Math Toolbox functions from the Help Desk. Also, you can print the PDF version of the *Symbolic Math Toolbox User's Guide* (tutorial and reference information) by selecting **Symbolic Math Toolbox User's Guide** from **Online Manuals** on the Help Desk.

Getting Help

There are several ways to find information on using Symbolic Math Toolbox functions. One, of course, is to read this chapter! Another is to use the Help Desk, which contains reference information for all the functions. You can also use MATLAB's command line help system. Generally, you can obtain help on MATLAB functions simply by typing

```
help function
```

where *function* is the name of the MATLAB function for which you need help. This is not sufficient, however, for some Symbolic Math Toolbox functions. The reason? The Symbolic Math Toolbox "overloads" many of MATLAB's numeric functions. That is, it provides symbolic-specific implementations of the functions, using the same function name. To obtain help for the symbolic version of an overloaded function, type

```
help sym/function
```

where *function* is the overloaded function's name. For example, to obtain help on the symbolic version of the overloaded function, diff, type

```
help sym/diff
```

To obtain information on the numeric version, on the other hand, simply type

```
help diff
```

How can you tell whether a function is overloaded? The help for the numeric version tells you so. For example, the help for the diff function contains the section

```
Overloaded methods
    help char/diff.m
    help sym/diff.m
```

This tells you that there are two other diff commands that operate on expressions of class char and class sym, respectively. See the next section for information on class sym. For more information on overloaded commands, see the *Using MATLAB* guide, which is accessible from the Help Desk.

Getting Started

This section describes how to create and use symbolic objects. It also describes the default symbolic variable. If you are familiar with version 1 of the Symbolic Math Toolbox, please note that version 2 uses substantially different and simpler syntax.

To get a quick online introduction to the Symbolic Math Toolbox, type demos at the MATLAB command line. MATLAB displays the **MATLAB Demos** dialog box. Select **Symbolic Math** (in the left list box) and then **Introduction** (in the right list box).

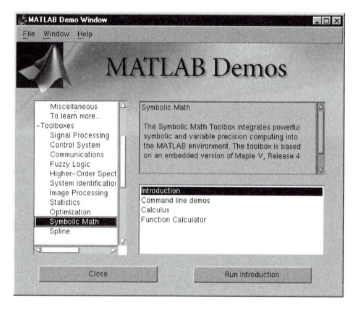

Symbolic Objects

The Symbolic Math Toolbox defines a new MATLAB data type called a symbolic object or sym (see *Using MATLAB* for an introduction to MATLAB classes and objects). Internally, a symbolic object is a data structure that stores a string representation of the symbol. The Symbolic Math Toolbox uses symbolic objects to represent symbolic variables, expressions, and matrices.

Creating Symbolic Variables and Expressions

The sym command lets you construct symbolic variables and expressions. For example, the commands

```
x = sym('x')
a = sym('alpha')
```

create a symbolic variable x that prints as x and a symbolic variable a that prints as alpha.

Suppose you want to use a symbolic variable to represent the golden ratio

$$\rho = \frac{1 + \sqrt{5}}{2}$$

The command

```
rho = sym('(1 + sqrt(5))/2')
```

achieves this goal. Now you can perform various mathematical operations on rho. For example,

```
f = rho^2 - rho - 1
```

returns

```
f =

(1/2+1/2*5^(1/2))^2-3/2-1/2*5^(1/2)
```

Then

```
simplify(f)
```

returns

```
0
```

Now suppose you want to study the quadratic function $f = ax^2 + bx + c$. The statement

```
f = sym('a*x^2 + b*x + c')
```

assigns the symbolic expression $ax^2 + bx + c$ to the variable f. Observe that in this case, the Symbolic Math Toolbox does not create variables corresponding to the terms of the expression, a, b, c, and x. To perform symbolic math operations (e.g., integration, differentiation, substitution, etc.) on f, you need to create the variables explicitly. You can do this by typing

```
a = sym('a')
b = sym('b')
c = sym('c')
x = sym('x')
```

or simply

```
syms a b c x
```

In general, you can use sym or syms to create symbolic variables. We recommend you use syms because it requires less typing.

Symbolic and Numeric Conversions

Consider the ordinary MATLAB quantity

```
t = 0.1
```

The sym function has four options for returning a symbolic representation of the numeric value stored in t. The 'f' option

```
sym(t,'f')
```

returns a symbolic floating-point representation

```
'1.999999999999a'*2^(-4)
```

The 'r' option

```
sym(t,'r')
```

returns the rational form

```
1/10
```

This is the default setting for sym. That is, calling sym without a second argument is the same as using sym with the 'r' option.

```
sym(t)

ans =
1/10
```

The third option `'e'` returns the rational form of t plus the difference between the theoretical rational expression for t and its actual (machine) floating-point value in terms of eps (the floating-point relative accuracy).

```
sym(t,'e')

ans =
1/10+eps/40
```

The fourth option `'d'` returns the decimal expansion of t up to the number of significant digits specified by `digits`.

```
sym(t,'d')

ans =
.10000000000000000555111512312578
```

The default value of `digits` is 32 (hence, `sym(t,'d')` returns a number with 32 significant digits), but if you prefer a shorter representation, use the `digits` command as follows.

```
digits(7)
sym(t,'d')

ans =
.1000000
```

A particularly effective use of sym is to convert a matrix from numeric to symbolic form. The command

```
A = hilb(3)
```

generates the 3-by-3 Hilbert matrix.

```
A =

     1.0000     0.5000     0.3333
     0.5000     0.3333     0.2500
     0.3333     0.2500     0.2000
```

By applying sym to A

```
A = sym(A)
```

you can obtain the (infinitely precise) symbolic form of the 3-by-3 Hilbert matrix.

```
A =

[   1, 1/2, 1/3]
[ 1/2, 1/3, 1/4]
[ 1/3, 1/4, 1/5]
```

Constructing Real and Complex Variables

The sym command allows you to specify the mathematical properties of symbolic variables by using the 'real' option. That is, the statements

```
x = sym('x','real'); y = sym('y','real');
```

or more efficiently

```
syms x y real
z = x + i*y
```

create symbolic variables x and y that have the added mathematical property of being real variables. Specifically this means that the expression

```
f = x^2 + y^2
```

is strictly nonnegative. Hence, z is a (formal) complex variable and can be manipulated as such. Thus, the commands

```
conj(x), conj(z), expand(z*conj(z))
```

return the complex conjugates of the variables

```
x, x - i*y, x^2 + y^2
```

The conj command is the complex conjugate operator for the toolbox. If conj(x) == x returns 1, then x is a real variable.

To clear x of its "real" property, you must type

```
syms x unreal
```

or

```
x = sym('x','unreal')
```

The command

```
clear x
```

does *not* make x a nonreal variable.

Creating Abstract Functions

If you want to create an abstract (i.e., indeterminant) function $f(x)$, type

```
f = sym('f(x)')
```

Then f acts like $f(x)$ and can be manipulated by the toolbox commands. To construct the first difference ratio, for example, type

```
df = (subs(f,'x','x+h') - f)/'h'
```

or

```
syms x h
df = (subs(f,x,x+h)-f)/h
```

which returns

```
df =
(f(x+h)-f(x))/h
```

This application of sym is useful when computing Fourier, Laplace, and z-transforms.

Example: Creating a Symbolic Matrix

A circulant matrix has the property that each row is obtained from the previous one by cyclically permuting the entries one step forward. We create the circulant matrix A whose elements are a, b, and c, using the commands

```
syms a b c
A = [a b c; b c a; c a b]
```

which return

```
A =
[ a, b, c ]
[ b, c, a ]
[ c, a, b ]
```

Since A is circulant, the sum over each row and column is the same. Let's check this for the first row and second column. The command

```
sum(A(1,:))
```

returns

```
ans =
a+b+c
```

The command

```
sum(A(1,:)) == sum(A(:,2)) % This is a logical test.
```

returns

```
ans =
     1
```

Now replace the (2,3) entry of A with beta and the variable b with alpha. The commands

```
syms alpha beta;
A(2,3) = beta;
A = subs(A,b,alpha)
```

return

```
A =
[     a, alpha,     c]
[ alpha,     c, beta]
[     c,     a, alpha]
```

From this example, you can see that using symbolic objects is very similar to using regular MATLAB numeric objects.

The Default Symbolic Variable

When manipulating mathematical functions, the choice of the independent variable is often clear from context. For example, consider the expressions in the table below.

Mathematical Function	MATLAB Command
$f = x^n$	`f = x^n`
$g = \sin(at+b)$	`g = sin(a*t + b)`
$h = J_v(z)$	`h = besselj(nu,z)`

If we ask for the derivatives of these expressions, without specifying the independent variable, then by mathematical convention we obtain $f' = nx^n$, $g' = a\cos(at + b)$, and $h' = J_v(z)(v/z) - J_{v+1}(z)$. Let's assume that the independent variables in these three expressions are x, t, and z, respectively. The other symbols, n, a, b, and v, are usually regarded as "constants" or "parameters." If, however, we wanted to differentiate the first expression with respect to n, for example, we could write

$$\frac{d}{dn}f(x) \ \text{ or } \ \frac{d}{dn}x^n$$

to get $x^n \ln x$.

By mathematical convention, independent variables are often lower-case letters found near the end of the Latin alphabet (e.g., x, y, or z). This is the idea behind `findsym`, a utility function in the toolbox used to determine default symbolic variables. Default symbolic variables are utilized by the calculus, simplification, equation-solving, and transform functions. To apply this utility to the example discussed above, type

```
syms a b n nu t x z
f = x^n; g = sin(a*t + b); h = besselj(nu,z);
```

This creates the symbolic expressions f, g, and h to match the example. To differentiate these expressions, we use `diff`.

```
diff(f)
```

returns

```
ans =
x^n*n/x
```

See the section "Differentiation" for a more detailed discussion of differentiation and the `diff` command.

Here, as above, we did not specify the variable with respect to differentiation. How did the toolbox determine that we wanted to differentiate with respect to x? The answer is the `findsym` command

```
findsym(f,1)
```

which returns

```
ans =
x
```

Similarly, `findsym(g,1)` and `findsym(h,1)` return t and z, respectively. Here the second argument of `findsym` denotes the number of symbolic variables we want to find in the symbolic object f, using the `findsym` rule (see below). The absence of a second argument in `findsym` results in a list of all symbolic variables in a given symbolic expression. We see this demonstrated below. The command

```
findsym(g)
```

returns the result

```
ans =
a, b, t
```

---

findsym Rule The default symbolic variable in a symbolic expression is the letter that is closest to `'x'` alphabetically. If there are two equally close, the letter later in the alphabet is chosen.

Here are some examples.

Expression	Variable Returned By findsym
x^n	x
sin(a*t+b)	t
besselj(nu,z)	z
w*y + v*z	y
exp(i*theta)	theta
log(alpha*x1)	x1
y*(4+3*i) + 6*j	y
sqrt(pi*alpha)	alpha

Creating Symbolic Math Functions

There are two ways to create functions:

- Use symbolic expressions
- Create an M-file

Using Symbolic Expressions

The sequence of commands

```
syms x y z
r = sqrt(x^2 + y^2 + z^2)
t = atan(y/x)
f = sin(x*y)/(x*y)
```

generates the symbolic expressions r, t, and f. You can use diff, int, subs, and other Symbolic Math Toolbox functions to manipulate such expressions.

Creating an M-File

M-files permit a more general use of functions. Suppose, for example, you want to create the `sinc` function `sin(x)/x`. To do this, create an M-file in the `@sym` directory.

```
function z = sinc(x)
%SINC The symbolic sinc function
%      sin(x)/x. This function
%      accepts a sym as the input argument.
if isequal(x,sym(0))
   z = 1;
else
   z = sin(x)/x;
end
```

You can extend such examples to functions of several variables. For a more detailed discussion on object-oriented programming, see the *Using MATLAB* guide.

Calculus

The Symbolic Math Toolbox provides functions to do the basic operations of calculus; differentiation, limits, integration, summation, and Taylor series expansion. The following sections outline these functions.

Differentiation

Let's create a symbolic expression.

```
syms a x
f = sin(a*x)
```

Then

```
diff(f)
```

differentiates f with respect to its symbolic variable (in this case x), as determined by findsym.

```
ans =
cos(a*x)*a
```

To differentiate with respect to the variable a, type

```
diff(f,a)
```

which returns df/da

```
ans =
cos(a*x)*x
```

To calculate the second derivatives with respect to x and a, respectively, type

```
diff(f,2)
```

or

```
diff(f,x,2)
```

which return

```
ans =
-sin(a*x)*a^2
```

and

```
diff(f,a,2)
```

which returns

```
ans =
-sin(a*x)*x^2
```

Define a, b, x, n, t, and theta in the MATLAB workspace, using the sym command. The table below illustrates the diff command.

f	diff(f)
x^n	x^n*n/x
sin(a*t+b)	a*cos(a*t+b)
exp(i*theta)	i*exp(i*theta)

To differentiate the Bessel function of the first kind, besselj(nu,z), with respect to z, type

```
syms nu z
b = besselj(nu,z);
db = diff(b)
```

which returns

```
db =
-besselj(nu+1,z)+nu/z*besselj(nu,z)
```

The diff function can also take a symbolic matrix as its input. In this case, the differentiation is done element-by-element. Consider the example

```
syms a x
A = [cos(a*x),sin(a*x);-sin(a*x),cos(a*x)]
```

which returns

```
A =
[  cos(a*x),   sin(a*x)]
[ -sin(a*x),   cos(a*x)]
```

The command

```
diff(A)
```

returns

```
ans =
[ -sin(a*x)*a,   cos(a*x)*a]
[ -cos(a*x)*a,  -sin(a*x)*a]
```

You can also perform differentiation of a column vector with respect to a row vector. Consider the transformation from Euclidean (x, y, z) to spherical (r, λ, φ) coordinates as given by $x = r \cos \lambda \cos \varphi$, $y = r \cos \lambda \sin \varphi$, and $z = r \sin \lambda$. Note that λ corresponds to elevation or latitude while φ denotes azimuth or longitude.

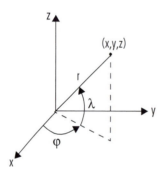

To calculate the Jacobian matrix, J, of this transformation, use the jacobian function. The mathematical notation for J is

$$J = \frac{\partial(x, y, x)}{\partial(r, \lambda, \varphi)}$$

For the purposes of toolbox syntax, we use l for λ and f for φ. The commands

```
syms r l f
x = r*cos(l)*cos(f); y = r*cos(l)*sin(f); z = r*sin(l);
J = jacobian([x; y; z], [r l f])
```

return the Jacobian

```
J =

[    cos(l)*cos(f),  -r*sin(l)*cos(f),  -r*cos(l)*sin(f)]
[    cos(l)*sin(f),  -r*sin(l)*sin(f),   r*cos(l)*cos(f)]
[           sin(l),         r*cos(l),                  0]
```

and the command

```
detJ = simple(det(J))
```

returns

```
detJ =
-cos(l)*r^2
```

Notice that the first argument of the jacobian function must be a column vector and the second argument a row vector. Moreover, since the determinant of the Jacobian is a rather complicated trigonometric expression, we used the simple command to make trigonometric substitutions and reductions (simplifications). The section "Simplifications and Substitutions" discusses simplification in more detail.

A table summarizing diff and jacobian follows.

Mathematical Operator	MATLAB Command
$\dfrac{df}{dx}$	diff(f) or diff(f,x)
$\dfrac{df}{da}$	diff(f,a)
$\dfrac{d^2 f}{db^2}$	diff(f,b,2)
$J = \dfrac{\partial(r, t)}{\partial(u, v)}$	J = jacobian([r:t],[u,v])

Limits

The fundamental idea in calculus is to make calculations on functions as a variable "gets close to" or approaches a certain value. Recall that the definition of the derivative is given by a limit

$$f'(x) = \lim_{h \to 0} \frac{f(x+h) - f(x)}{h}$$

provided this limit exists. The Symbolic Math Toolbox allows you to compute the limits of functions in a direct manner. The commands

```
syms h n x
limit( (cos(x+h) - cos(x))/h,h,0 )
```

which return

```
ans =
-sin(x)
```

and

```
limit( (1 + x/n)^n,n,inf )
```

which returns

```
ans =
exp(x)
```

illustrate two of the most important limits in mathematics: the derivative (in this case of cos x) and the exponential function. While many limits

$$\lim_{x \to a} f(x)$$

are "two sided" (that is, the result is the same whether the approach is from the right or left of a), limits at the singularities of $f(x)$ are not. Hence, the three limits,

$$\lim_{x \to 0} \frac{1}{x} , \ \lim_{x \to 0-} \frac{1}{x} , \text{ and } \lim_{x \to 0+} \frac{1}{x}$$

yield the three distinct results: undefined, $-\infty$, and $+\infty$, respectively.

In the case of undefined limits, the Symbolic Math Toolbox returns NaN (not a number). The command

```
limit(1/x,x,0)
```

or

```
limit(1/x)
```

returns

```
ans =
NaN
```

The command

```
limit(1/x,x,0,'left')
```

returns

```
ans =
-inf
```

while the command

```
limit(1/x,x,0,'right')
```

returns

```
ans =
inf
```

Observe that the default case, limit(f) is the same as limit(f,x,0). Explore the options for the limit command in this table. Here, we assume that f is a function of the symbolic object x.

Mathematical Operation	MATLAB Command
$\lim_{x \to 0} f(x)$	limit(f)
$\lim_{x \to a} f(x)$	limit(f,x,a) or limit(f,a)

Mathematical Operation	MATLAB Command
$\lim_{x \to a-} f(x)$	`limit(f,x,a,'left')`
$\lim_{x \to a+} f(x)$	`limit(f,x,a,'right')`

Integration

If f is a symbolic expression, then

```
int(f)
```

attempts to find another symbolic expression, F, so that `diff(F) = f`. That is, `int(f)` returns the indefinite integral or antiderivative of f (provided one exists in closed form). Similar to differentiation,

```
int(f,v)
```

uses the symbolic object v as the variable of integration, rather than the variable determined by `findsym`. See how `int` works by looking at this table.

Mathematical Operation	MATLAB Command
$\int x^n dx = \dfrac{x^{n+1}}{n+1}$	`int(x^n)` or `int(x^n,x)`
$\displaystyle\int_0^{\pi/2} \sin(2x)dx = 1$	`int(sin(2*x),0,pi/2)` or `int(sin(2*x),x,0,pi/2)`

$g = \cos(at+b)$
 $\int g(t)dt = \sin(at+b)/a$
	`g = cos(a*t + b)`
	 `int(g)` or
	 `int(g,t)`

$\int J_1(z)dz = -J_0(z)$	`int(besselj(1,z))` or `int(besselj(1,z),z)`

In contrast to differentiation, symbolic integration is a more complicated task. A number of difficulties can arise in computing the integral. The antiderivative, F, may not exist in closed form; it may define an unfamiliar function; it may exist, but the software can't find the antiderivative; the software could find it on a larger computer, but runs out of time or memory on the available machine. Nevertheless, in many cases, MATLAB can perform symbolic integration successfully. For example, create the symbolic variables

```
syms a b theta x y n x1 u
```

This table illustrates integration of expressions containing those variables.

f	int(f)
x^n	x^(n+1)/(n+1)
y^(-1)	log(y)
n^x	1/log(n)*n^x
sin(a*theta+b)	-cos(a*theta+b)/a
exp(-x1^2)	1/2*pi^(1/2)*erf(x1)
1/(1+u^2)	atan(u)

The last example shows what happens if the toolbox can't find the antiderivative; it simply returns the command, including the variable of integration, unevaluated.

Definite integration is also possible. The commands

```
int(f,a,b)
```

and

```
int(f,v,a,b)
```

are used to find a symbolic expression for

$$\int_a^b f(x)dx \text{ and } \int_a^b f(v)dv$$

respectively.

Here are some additional examples.

f	a, b	int(f,a,b)
x^7	0, 1	1/8
1/x	1, 2	log(2)
log(x)*sqrt(x)	0, 1	-4/9
exp(-x^2)	0, inf	1/2*pi^(1/2)
bessel(1,z)	0, 1	-besselj(0,1)+1

For the Bessel function (besselj) example, it is possible to compute a numerical approximation to the value of the integral, using the double function. The command

```
a = int(besselj(1,z),0,1)
```

returns

```
a =
-besselj(0,1)+1
```

and the command

```
a = double(a)
```

returns

```
a =
   0.23480231344203
```

Integration with Real Constants

One of the subtleties involved in symbolic integration is the "value" of various parameters. For example, the expression

$$e^{-(kx)^2}$$

is the positive, bell shaped curve that tends to 0 as x tends to $\pm\infty$ for any real number k. An example of this curve is depicted below with

$$k = \frac{1}{\sqrt{2}}$$

and generated, using these commands.

```
syms x
k = sym(1/sqrt(2));
f = exp(-(k*x)^2);
ezplot(f)
```

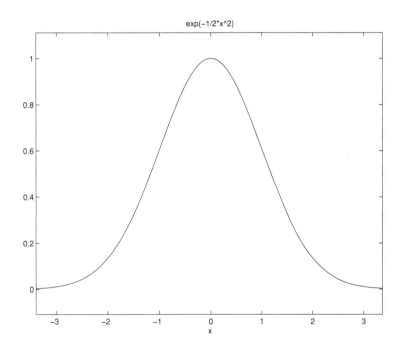

The Maple kernel, however, does not, *a priori,* treat the expressions k^2 or x^2 as positive numbers. To the contrary, Maple assumes that the symbolic variables x and k as *a priori* indeterminate. That is, they are purely formal variables with no mathematical properties. Consequently, the initial attempt to compute the integral

$$\int\limits_{-\infty}^{\infty} e^{-(kx)^2} dx$$

in the Symbolic Math Toolbox, using the commands

```
syms x k;
f = exp(-(k*x)^2);
int(f,x,-inf,inf)
```

results in the output

```
Definite integration: Can't determine if the integral is
convergent.
Need to know the sign of --> k^2
Will now try indefinite integration and then take limits.

Warning: Explicit integral could not be found.
ans =
int(exp(-k^2*x^2),x= -inf..inf)
```

In the next section, you well see how to make k a real variable and therefore k^2 positive.

Real Variables via sym

Notice that Maple is not able to determine the sign of the expression k^2. How does one surmount this obstacle? The answer is to make k a real variable, using the sym command. One particularly useful feature of sym, namely the real option, allows you to declare k to be a real variable. Consequently, the integral above is computed, in the toolbox, using the sequence

```
syms k real
int(f,x,-inf,inf)
```

which returns

```
ans =
signum(k)/k*pi^(1/2)
```

Notice that k is now a symbolic object in the MATLAB workspace and a real variable in the Maple kernel workspace. By typing

```
clear k
```

you only clear k in the MATLAB workspace. To ensure that k has no formal properties (that is, to ensure k is a purely formal variable), type

```
syms k unreal
```

This variation of the syms command clears k in the Maple workspace. You can also declare a sequence of symbolic variables w, y, x, z to be real, using

```
syms w x y z real
```

In this case, all of the variables in between the words syms and real are assigned the property real. That is, they are real variables in the Maple workspace.

Symbolic Summation

You can compute symbolic summations, when they exist, by using the symsum command. For example, the p-series

$$1 + \frac{1}{2^2} + \frac{1}{3^2} + \ldots$$

adds to $\pi^2/6$, while the geometric series $1 + x + x^2 + \ldots$ adds to $1/(1-x)$, provided $|x| < 1$. Three summations are demonstrated below.

```
syms x k
s1 = symsum(1/k^2,1,inf)
s2 = symsum(x^k,k,0,inf)

s1 =

1/6*pi^2

s2 =

-1/(x-1)
```

Taylor Series

The statements

```
syms x
f = 1/(5+4*cos(x))
T = taylor(f,8)
```

return

```
T =
1/9+2/81*x^2+5/1458*x^4+49/131220*x^6
```

which is all the terms up to, but not including, order eight $(O(x^8))$ in the Taylor series for $f(x)$.

$$\sum_{n=0}^{\infty} (x-a)^n \, \frac{f^{(n)}(a)}{n!}$$

Technically, T is a Maclaurin series, since its basepoint is a = 0.

The command

```
pretty(T)
```

prints T in a format resembling typeset mathematics.

```
                2              4       49      6
   1/9 + 2/81 x   + 5/1458 x   + ------ x
                                  131220
```

These commands

```
syms x
g = exp(x*sin(x))
t = taylor(g,12,2)
```

generate the first 12 nonzero terms of the Taylor series for g about x = 2.

Let's plot these functions together to see how well this Taylor approximation compares to the actual function g.

```
xd = 1:0.05:3; yd = subs(g,x,xd);
ezplot(t, [1,3]); hold on;
plot(xd, yd, 'r-.')
title('Taylor approximation vs. actual function');
legend('Function','Taylor')
```

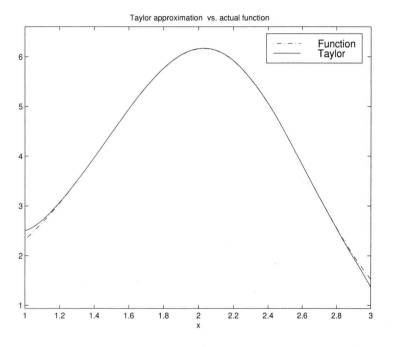

Special thanks to Professor Gunnar Bäckstrøm of UMEA in Sweden for this example.

Extended Calculus Example

The function

$$f(x) = \frac{1}{5 + 4\cos(x)}$$

provides a starting point for illustrating several calculus operations in the toolbox. It is also an interesting function in its own right. The statements

```
syms x
f = 1/(5+4*cos(x))
```

store the symbolic expression defining the function in f.

The function ezplot(f) produces the plot of *f(x)* as shown below.

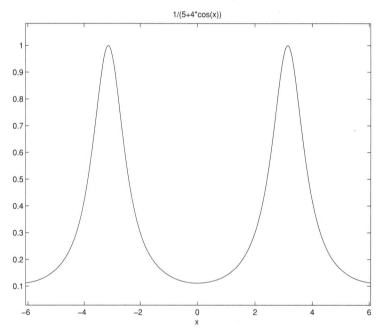

The ezplot function tries to make reasonable choices for the range of the *x*-axis and for the resulting scale of the *y*-axis. Its choices can be overridden by an additional input argument, or by subsequent axis commands. The default domain for a function displayed by ezplot is $-2\pi \le x \le 2\pi$. To produce a graph of $f(x)$ for $a \le x \le b$, type

```
ezplot(f,[a b])
```

Let's now look at the second derivative of the function f.

```
f2 = diff(f,2)

f2 =
32/(5+4*cos(x))^3*sin(x)^2+4/(5+4*cos(x))^2*cos(x)
```

Equivalently, we can type f2 = diff(f,x,2). The default scaling in ezplot cuts off part of f2's graph. Set the axes limits manually to see the entire function.

```
ezplot(f2)
axis([-2*pi 2*pi -5 2])
```

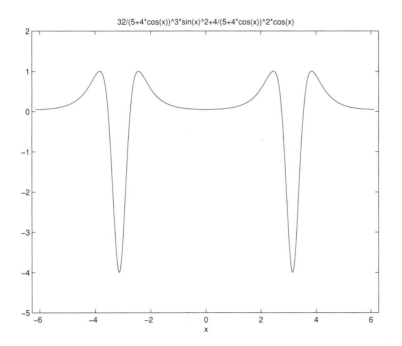

From the graph, it appears that the values of $f''(x)$ lie between -4 and 1. As it turns out, this is not true. We can calculate the exact range for f (i.e., compute its actual maximum and minimum).

The actual maxima and minima of $f''(x)$ occur at the zeros of $f'''(x)$. The statements

```
f3 = diff(f2);
pretty(f3)
```

compute $f'''(x)$ and display it in a more readable format.

```
                  3
                sin(x)            sin(x) cos(x)            sin(x)
        384 --------------- + 96 -------------- - 4 ---------------
                     4                    3                      2
            (5 + 4 cos(x))        (5 + 4 cos(x))         (5 + 4 cos(x))
```

We can simplify this expression using the statements

```
f3 = simple(f3);
pretty(f3)
```

```
                             2                       2
            sin(x) (96 sin(x)  + 80 cos(x) + 80 cos(x)  - 25)
        4 ---------------------------------------------------
                                      4
                            (5 + 4 cos(x))
```

Now use the solve function to find the zeros of $f'''(x)$.

```
z = solve(f3)
```

returns a 5-by-1 symbolic matrix

```
z =
[                                                        0]
[        atan((-255-60*19^(1/2))^(1/2),10+3*19^(1/2))]
[        atan(-(-255-60*19^(1/2))^(1/2),10+3*19^(1/2))]
[   atan((-255+60*19^(1/2))^(1/2)/(10-3*19^(1/2)))+pi]
[   -atan((-255+60*19^(1/2))^(1/2)/(10-3*19^(1/2)))-pi]
```

each of whose entries is a zero of $f'''(x)$. The command

```
format; % Default format of 5 digits
zr = double(z)
```

converts the zeros to double form.

```
zr =

        0
        0+ 2.4381i
        0- 2.4381i
   2.4483
  -2.4483
```

So far, we have found three real zeros and two complex zeros. However, a graph of f3 shows that we have not yet found all its zeros.

```
ezplot(f3)
hold on;
plot(zr,0*zr,'ro')
plot([-2*pi,2*pi], [0,0],'g-.');
title('Zeros of f3')
```

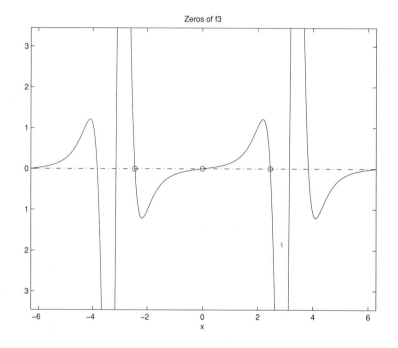

This occurs because $f'''(x)$ contains a factor of $\sin(x)$, which is zero at integer multiples of π. The function, solve(sin(x)), however, only reports the zero at $x = 0$.

We can obtain a complete list of the real zeros by translating zr

```
zr = [0 zr(4) pi 2*pi-zr(4)]
```

by multiples of 2π

```
zr = [zr-2*pi zr zr+2*pi];
```

Now let's plot the transformed zr on our graph for a complete picture of the zeros of f3.

```
plot(zr,0*zr,'kX')
```

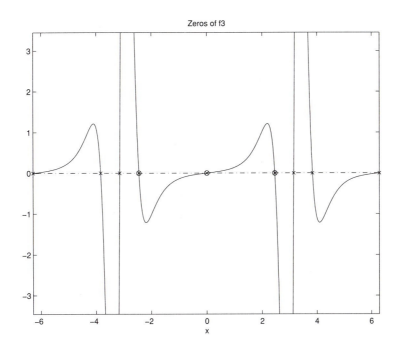

The first zero of $f'''(x)$ found by solve is at $x = 0$. We substitute 0 for the symbolic variable in f2

```
f20 = subs(f2,x,0)
```

to compute the corresponding value of $f''(0)$.

```
f20 =
    0.0494
```

A look at the graph of $f''(x)$ shows that this is only a local minimum, which we demonstrate by replotting f2.

```
clf
ezplot(f2)
axis([-2*pi 2*pi -4.25 1.25])
ylabel('f2');
title('Plot of f2 = f''''(x)')
hold on
plot(0,double(f20),'ro')
text(-1,-0.25,'Local minimum')
```

The resulting plot

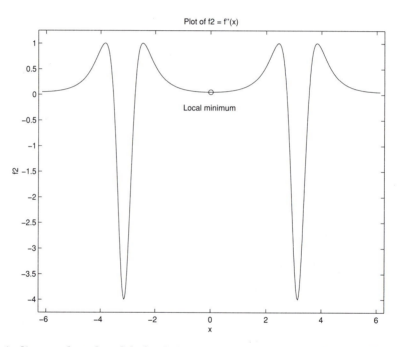

indicates that the global minima occur near $x = -\pi$ and $x = \pi$. We can demonstrate that they occur exactly at $x = \pm\pi$, using the following sequence of commands. First we try substituting $-\pi$ and π into $f''(x)$.

```
simple([subs(f3,x,-sym(pi)),subs(f3,x,sym(pi))])
```

The result

```
ans =
[ 0, 0]
```

shows that -π and π happen to be critical points of $f'''(x)$. We can see that -π and π are global minima by plotting f2(-pi) and f2(pi) against f2(x).

```
m1 = double(subs(f2,x,-pi)); m2 = double(subs(f2,x,pi));
plot(-pi,m1,'go',pi,m2,'go')
text(-1,-4,'Global minima')
```

The actual minima are m1, m2

```
ans =
[ -4, -4]
```

as shown in the following plot.

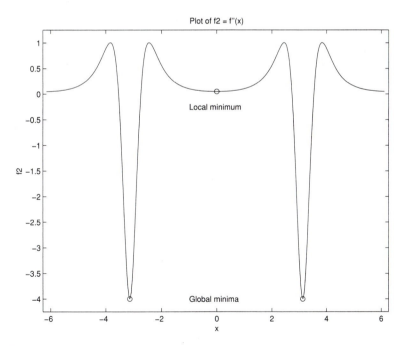

The foregoing analysis confirms part of our original guess that the range of $f''(x)$ is [-4, 1]. We can confirm the other part by examining the fourth zero of

$f'''(x)$ found by `solve`. First extract the fourth zero from `z` and assign it to a separate variable

```
s = z(4)
```

to obtain

```
s =
atan((-255+60*19^(1/2))^(1/2)/(10-3*19^(1/2)))+pi
```

Executing

```
sd = double(s)
```

displays the zero's corresponding numeric value.

```
sd =
2.4483
```

Plotting the point (`s`, `f2(s)`) against `f2`, using

```
M1 = double(subs(f2,x,s));
plot(sd,M1,'ko')
text(-1,1,'Global maximum')
```

visually confirms that s is a maximum.

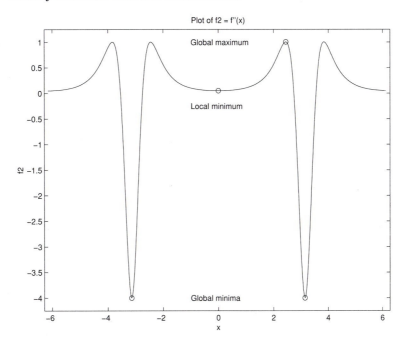

The maximum is M1 = 1.0051.

Therefore, our guess that the maximum of $f''(x)$ is [-4, 1] was close, but incorrect. The actual range is [-4, 1.0051].

Now, let's see if integrating $f''(x)$ twice with respect to x recovers our original function $f(x) = 1/(5 + 4 \cos x)$. The command

```
g = int(int(f2))
```

returns

```
g =
-8/(tan(1/2*x)^2+9)
```

This is certainly not the original expression for $f(x)$. Let's look at the difference $f(x) - g(x)$.

```
d = f - g
pretty(d)
```

$$\frac{1}{5 + 4\cos(x)} + \frac{8}{\tan(1/2\ x)^2 + 9}$$

We can simplify this using `simple(d)` or `simplify(d)`. Either command produces

```
ans =
1
```

This illustrates the concept that differentiating $f(x)$ twice, then integrating the result twice, produces a function that may differ from $f(x)$ by a linear function of x.

Finally, integrate $f(x)$ once more.

```
F = int(f)
```

The result

```
F =
2/3*atan(1/3*tan(1/2*x))
```

involves the arctangent function.

Though $F(x)$ is the antiderivative of a continuous function, it is itself discontinuous as the following plot shows.

ezplot(F)

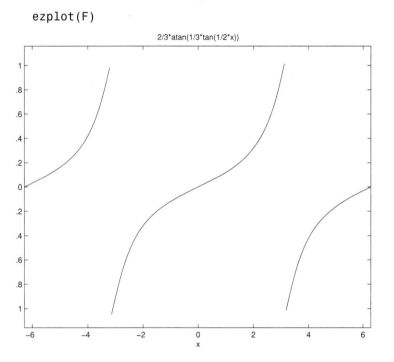

Note that $F(x)$ has jumps at $x = \pm \pi$. This occurs because tan x is singular at $x = \pm \pi$.

In fact, as

```
ezplot(atan(tan(x)))
```

shows, the numerical value of `atan(tan(x))` differs from x by a piecewise constant function that has jumps at odd multiples of π/2.

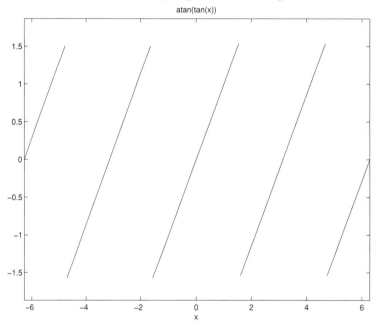

To obtain a representation of *F(x)* that does not have jumps at these points, we must introduce a second function, *J(x)*, that compensates for the discontinuities. Then we add the appropriate multiple of *J(x)* to *F(x)*

```
J = sym('round(x/(2*pi))');
c = sym('2/3*pi');
F1 = F+c*J
F1 =
2/3*atan(1/3*tan(1/2*x))+2/3*pi*round(1/2*x/pi)
```

and plot the result.

```
ezplot(F1,[-6.28,6.28])
```

This representation does have a continuous graph.

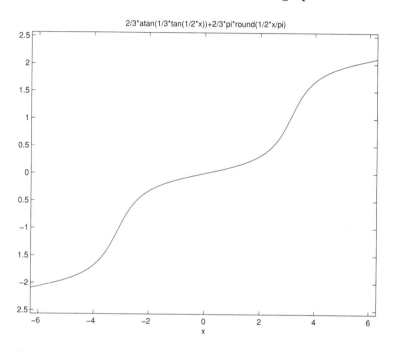

Notice that we use the domain [-6.28, 6.28] in `ezplot` rather than the default domain [-2π, 2π]. The reason for this is to prevent an evaluation of $F1 = 2/3 \text{ atan}(1/3 \tan 1/2\, x)$ at the singular points $x = -\pi$ and $x = \pi$ where the jumps in F and J do not cancel out one another. The proper handling of branch cut discontinuities in multivalued functions like arctan x is a deep and difficult problem in symbolic computation. Although MATLAB and Maple cannot do this entirely automatically, they do provide the tools for investigating such questions.

Simplifications and Substitutions

There are several functions that simplify symbolic expressions and are used to perform symbolic substitutions.

Simplifications

Here are three different symbolic expressions.

```
syms x
f = x^3-6*x^2+11*x-6
g = (x-1)*(x-2)*(x-3)
h = x*(x*(x-6)+11)-6
```

Here are their prettyprinted forms, generated by

```
pretty(f), pretty(g), pretty(h)

 3     2
x - 6 x  + 11 x - 6


(x - 1) (x - 2) (x - 3)


x (x (x - 6) + 11) - 6
```

These expressions are three different representations of the same mathematical function, a cubic polynomial in x.

Each of the three forms is preferable to the others in different situations. The first form, f, is the most commonly used representation of a polynomial. It is simply a linear combination of the powers of x. The second form, g, is the factored form. It displays the roots of the polynomial and is the most accurate for numerical evaluation near the roots. But, if a polynomial does not have such simple roots, its factored form may not be so convenient. The third form, h, is the Horner, or nested, representation. For numerical evaluation, it involves the fewest arithmetic operations and is the most accurate for some other ranges of x.

The symbolic simplification problem involves the verification that these three expressions represent the same function. It also involves a less clearly defined objective — which of these representations is "the simplest"?

This toolbox provides several functions that apply various algebraic and trigonometric identities to transform one representation of a function into another, possibly simpler, representation. These functions are collect, expand, horner, factor, simplify, and simple.

collect

The statement

```
collect(f)
```

views f as a polynomial in its symbolic variable, say x, and collects all the coefficients with the same power of x. A second argument can specify the variable in which to collect terms if there is more than one candidate. Here are a few examples.

f	collect(f)
(x-1)*(x-2)*(x-3)	x^3-6*x^2+11*x-6
x*(x*(x-6)+11)-6	x^3-6*x^2+11*x-6
(1+x)*t + x*t	2*x*t+t

expand

The statement

    expand(f)

distributes products over sums and applies other identities involving functions of sums. For example,

f	expand(f)
a*(x + y)	a*x + a*y
(x-1)*(x-2)*(x-3)	x^3-6*x^2+11*x-6
x*(x*(x-6)+11)-6	x^3-6*x^2+11*x-6
exp(a+b)	exp(a)*exp(b)
cos(x+y)	cos(x)*cos(y)-sin(x)*sin(y)
cos(3*acos(x))	4*x^3 - 3*x

horner

The statement

    horner(f)

transforms a symbolic polynomial f into its Horner, or nested, representation. For example,

f	horner(f)
x^3-6*x^2+11*x-6	-6+(11+(-6+x)*x)*x
1.1+2.2*x+3.3*x^2	11/10+(11/5+33/10*x)*x

factor

If f is a polynomial with rational coefficients, the statement

```
factor(f)
```

expresses f as a product of polynomials of lower degree with rational coefficients. If f cannot be factored over the rational numbers, the result is f itself. For example,

f	factor(f)
x^3-6*x^2+11*x-6	(x-1)*(x-2)*(x-3)
x^3-6*x^2+11*x-5	x^3-6*x^2+11*x-5
x^6+1	(x^2+1)*(x^4-x^2+1)

Here is another example involving factor. It factors polynomials of the form x^n + 1. This code

```
syms x;
n = (1:9)';
p = x.^n + 1;
f = factor(p);
[p, f]
```

returns a matrix with the polynomials in its first column and their factored forms in its second.

```
[                               x+1,                                    x+1 ]
[                             x^2+1,                                  x^2+1 ]
[                             x^3+1,                    (x+1)*(x^2-x+1) ]
[                             x^4+1,                                  x^4+1 ]
[                             x^5+1,        (x+1)*(x^4-x^3+x^2-x+1) ]
[                             x^6+1,              (x^2+1)*(x^4-x^2+1) ]
[                             x^7+1, (x+1)*(1-x+x^2-x^3+x^4-x^5+x^6) ]
[                             x^8+1,                                  x^8+1 ]
[                             x^9+1,        (x+1)*(x^2-x+1)*(x^6-x^3+1) ]
```

As an aside at this point, we mention that `factor` can also factor symbolic objects containing integers. This is an alternative to using the `factor` function in MATLAB's `specfun` directory. For example, the following code segment

```
N = sym(1);
for k = 2:11
    N(k) = 10*N(k-1)+1;
end
[N' factor(N')]
```

displays the factors of symbolic integers consisting of 1s.

```
[                     1,                            1]
[                    11,                         (11)]
[                   111,                    (3)*(37)]
[                  1111,                 (11)*(101)]
[                 11111,                 (41)*(271)]
[                111111, (3)*(7)*(11)*(13)*(37)]
[               1111111,             (239)*(4649)]
[              11111111,    (11)*(73)*(101)*(137)]
[             111111111,       (3)^2*(37)*(333667)]
[            1111111111, (11)*(41)*(271)*(9091)]
[           11111111111,        (513239)*(21649)]
```

simplify

The simplify function is a powerful, general purpose tool that applies a number of algebraic identities involving sums, integral powers, square roots and other fractional powers, as well as a number of functional identities involving trig functions, exponential and log functions, Bessel functions, hypergeometric functions, and the gamma function. Here are some examples.

f	simplify(f)
x*(x*(x-6)+11)-6	x^3-6*x^2+11*x-6
(1-x^2)/(1-x)	x+1
(1/a^3+6/a^2+12/a+8)^(1/3)	((2*a+1)^3/a^3)^(1/3)
syms x y positive log(x*y)	log(x)+log(y)
exp(x) * exp(y)	exp(x+y)
besselj(2,x) + besselj(0,x)	2/x*besselj(1,x)
gamma(x+1)-x*gamma(x)	0
cos(x)^2 + sin(x)^2	1

simple

The simple function has the unorthodox mathematical goal of finding a simplification of an expression that has the fewest number of characters. Of course, there is little mathematical justification for claiming that one expression is "simpler" than another just because its ASCII representation is shorter, but this often proves satisfactory in practice.

The simple function achieves its goal by independently applying simplify, collect, factor, and other simplification functions to an expression and keeping track of the lengths of the results. The simple function then returns the shortest result.

The simple function has several forms, each returning different output. The form

```
simple(f)
```

displays each trial simplification and the simplification function that produced it in the MATLAB command window. The `simple` function then returns the shortest result. For example, the command

```
simple(cos(x)^2 + sin(x)^2)
```

displays the following alternative simplifications in the MATLAB command window

```
simplify:
1

radsimp:
cos(x)^2+sin(x)^2

combine(trig):
1

factor:
cos(x)^2+sin(x)^2

expand:
cos(x)^2+sin(x)^2

convert(exp):
(1/2*exp(i*x)+1/2/exp(i*x))^2-1/4*(exp(i*x)-1/exp(i*x))^2

convert(sincos):
cos(x)^2+sin(x)^2


convert(tan):
(1-tan(1/2*x)^2)^2/(1+tan(1/2*x)^2)^2+4*tan(1/2*x)^2/
(1+tan(1/2*x)^2)^2

collect(x):
cos(x)^2+sin(x)^2
```

and returns

```
ans =
1
```

This form is useful when you want to check, for example, whether the shortest form is indeed the simplest. If you are not interested in how `simple` achieves its result, use the form

```
f = simple(f)
```

This form simply returns the shortest expression found. For example, the statement

```
f = simple(cos(x)^2+sin(x)^2)
```

returns

```
f =
1
```

If you want to know which simplification returned the shortest result, use the multiple output form.

```
[F, how] = simple(f)
```

This form returns the shortest result in the first variable and the simplification method used to achieve the result in the second variable. For example, the statement

```
[f, how] = simple(cos(x)^2+sin(x)^2)
```

returns

```
f =
1

how =
combine
```

The `simple` function sometimes improves on the result returned by `simplify`, one of the simplifications that it tries. For example, when applied to the examples given for `simplify`, `simple` returns a simpler (or at least shorter) result in two cases.

f	simplify(f)	simple(f)
`(1/a^3+6/a^2+12/a+8)^(1/3)`	`((2*a+1)^3/a^3)^(1/3)`	`(2*a+1)/a`
`syms x y positive` `log(x*y)`	`log(x)+log(y)`	`log(x*y)`

In some cases, it is advantageous to apply `simple` twice to obtain the effect of two different simplification functions. For example, the statements

```
f = (1/a^3+6/a^2+12/a+8)^(1/3);
simple(simple(f))
```

return

```
1/a+2
```

The first application, `simple(f)`, uses `radsimp` to produce `(2*a+1)/a`; the second application uses `combine(trig)` to transform this to `1/a+2`.

The `simple` function is particularly effective on expressions involving trigonometric functions. Here are some examples.

f	simple(f)
`cos(x)^2+sin(x)^2`	`1`
`2*cos(x)^2-sin(x)^2`	`3*cos(x)^2-1`
`cos(x)^2-sin(x)^2`	`cos(2*x)`
`cos(x)+(-sin(x)^2)^(1/2)`	`cos(x)+i*sin(x)`
`cos(x)+i*sin(x)`	`exp(i*x)`
`cos(3*acos(x))`	`4*x^3-3*x`

Substitutions

There are two functions for symbolic substitution: subexpr and subs.

subexpr

These commands

```
syms a x
s = solve(x^3+a*x+1)
```

solve the equation x^3+a*x+1 = 0 for x.

```
s =
[                                1/6*(-108+12*(12*a^3+81)^(1/2))^(1/3)-2*a/
                                    (-108+12*(12*a^3+81)^(1/2))^(1/3)]
[  -1/12*(-108+12*(12*a^3+81)^(1/2))^(1/3)+a/
      (-108+12*(12*a^3+81)^(1/2))^(1/3)+1/2*i*3^(1/2)*(1/
      6*(-108+12*(12*a^3+81)^(1/2))^(1/3)+2*a/
      (-108+12*(12*a^3+81)^(1/2))^(1/3))]
[  -1/12*(-108+12*(12*a^3+81)^(1/2))^(1/3)+a/
      (-108+12*(12*a^3+81)^(1/2))^(1/3)-1/2*i*3^(1/2)*(1/
      6*(-108+12*(12*a^3+81)^(1/2))^(1/3)+2*a/
      (-108+12*(12*a^3+81)^(1/2))^(1/3))]
```

Use the pretty function to display s in a more readable form.

```
pretty(s)
```

s =
```
[                                     1/3        a                      ]
[                        1/6 %1      - 2 -----                          ]
[                                              1/3                      ]
[                                             %1                        ]
[                                                                       ]
[         1/3      a            1/2 /      1/3        a \]
[- 1/12 %1     + ----- + 1/2 i 3  |1/6 %1    + 2 -----|]
[                 1/3             |                1/3|]
[                %1               \                %1  /]
[                                                                       ]
[         1/3      a            1/2 /      1/3        a \]
[- 1/12 %1     + ----- - 1/2 i 3  |1/6 %1    + 2 -----|]
[                 1/3             |                1/3|]
[                %1               \                %1  /]
```

```
                                      3        1/2
          %1 := -108 + 12 (12 a   + 81)
```

The pretty command inherits the %n (n, an integer) notation from Maple to denote subexpressions that occur multiple times in the symbolic object. The subexpr function allows you to save these common subexpressions as well as the symbolic object rewritten in terms of the subexpressions. The subexpressions are saved in a column vector called sigma.

Continuing with the example

```
r = subexpr(s)
```

returns

```
sigma =
-108+12*(12*a^3+81)^(1/2)

r =
[                                      1/6*sigma^(1/3)-2*a/sigma^(1/3)]
[ -1/12*sigma^(1/3)+a/sigma^(1/3)+1/2*i*3^(1/2)*(1/6*sigma^
    (1/3)+2*a/sigma^(1/3))]
[ -1/12*sigma^(1/3)+a/sigma^(1/3)-1/2*i*3^(1/2)*(1/6*sigma^
    (1/3)+2*a/sigma^(1/3))]
```

Notice that subexpr creates the variable sigma in the MATLAB workspace. You can verify this by typing whos, or the command

```
sigma
```

which returns

```
sigma =
-108+12*(12*a^3+81)^(1/2)
```

subs

Let's find the eigenvalues and eigenvectors of a circulant matrix A.

```
syms a b c
A = [a b c; b c a; c a b];
[v,E] = eig(A)

v =

[ -(a+(b^2-b*a-c*b-c*a+a^2+c^2)^(1/2)-b)/(a-c),
        -(a-(b^2-b*a-c*b-c*a+a^2+c^2)^(1/2)-b)/(a-c),   1]
[ -(b-c-(b^2-b*a-c*b-c*a+a^2+c^2)^(1/2))/(a-c),
        -(b-c+(b^2-b*a-c*b-c*a+a^2+c^2)^(1/2))/(a-c),   1]
[ 1,
            1,                                          1]


E =

[ (b^2-b*a-c*b-
    c*a+a^2+c^2)^(1/2),                       0,           0]
[               0,    -(b^2-b*a-c*b-
                        c*a+a^2+c^2)^(1/2),                0]
[               0,                        0,          b+c+a]
```

Suppose we want to replace the rather lengthy expression

```
(b^2-b*a-c*b-c*a+a^2+c^2)^(1/2)
```

throughout v and E. We first use subexpr

```
v = subexpr(v,'S')
```

which returns

```
S =
(b^2-b*a-c*b-c*a+a^2+c^2)^(1/2)

v =
[ -(a+S-b)/(a-c),  -(a-S-b)/(a-c),           1]
[ -(b-c-S)/(a-c),  -(b-c+S)/(a-c),           1]
[             1,               1,            1]
```

Next, substitute the symbol S into E with

```
E = subs(E,S,'S')

E =
[     S,     0,     0]
[     0,    -S,     0]
[     0,     0, b+c+a]
```

Now suppose we want to evaluate v at a = 10. We can do this using the subs command.

```
subs(v,a,10)
```

This replaces all occurrences of a in v with 10.

```
[ -(10+S-b)/(10-c), -(10-S-b)/(10-c),          1]
[  -(b-c-S)/(10-c),  -(b-c+S)/(10-c),          1]
[                1,                1,          1]
```

Notice, however, that the symbolic expression represented by S is unaffected by this substitution. That is, the symbol a in S is not replaced by 10. The subs command is also a useful function for substituting in a variety of values for several variables in a particular expression. Let's look at S. Suppose that in addition to substituting a = 10, we also want to substitute the values for 2 and 10 for b and c, respectively. The way to do this is to set values for a, b, and c in the workspace. Then subs evaluates its input using the existing symbolic and double variables in the current workspace. In our example, we first set

```
a = 10; b = 2; c = 10;
subs(S)

ans =
8
```

To look at the contents of our workspace, type whos, which gives

```
Name      Size          Bytes  Class

  A       3x3            878   sym object
  E       3x3            888   sym object
  S       1x1            186   sym object
  a       1x1              8   double array
  ans     1x1            140   sym object
  b       1x1              8   double array
  c       1x1              8   double array
  v       3x3            982   sym object
```

a, b, and c are now variables of class double while A, E, S, and v remain symbolic expressions (class sym).

If you want to preserve a, b, and c as symbolic variables, but still alter their value within S, use this procedure.

```
syms a b c
subs(S,{a,b,c},{10,2,10})

ans =
8
```

Typing whos reveals that a, b, and c remain 1-by-1 sym objects.

The subs command can be combined with double to evaluate a symbolic expression numerically. Suppose we have

```
syms t
M = (1-t^2)*exp(-1/2*t^2);
P = (1-t^2)*sech(t);
```

and want to see how M and P differ graphically.

One approach is to type

```
ezplot(M); hold on; ezplot(P)
```

but this plot

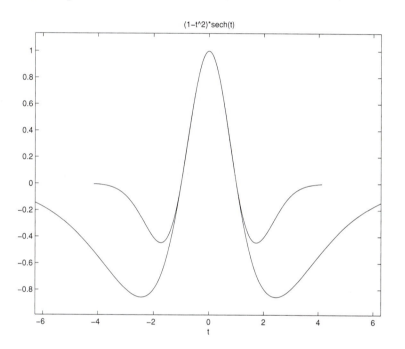

does not readily help us identify the curves.

Instead, combine subs, double, and plot

```
T = -6:0.05:6;
MT = double(subs(M,t,T));
PT = double(subs(P,t,T));
plot(T,MT,'b',T,PT,'r-.')
title(' ')
legend('M','P')
xlabel('t'); grid
```

to produce a multicolored graph that indicates the difference between M and P.

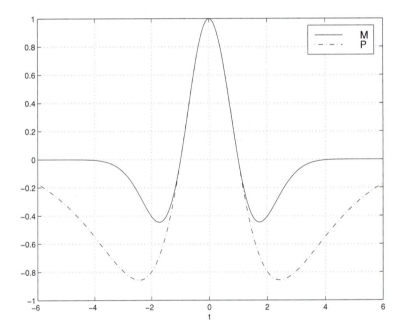

Finally the use of subs with strings greatly facilitates the solution of problems involving the Fourier, Laplace, or z-transforms.

Variable-Precision Arithmetic

Overview

There are three different kinds of arithmetic operations in this toolbox.

- Numeric   MATLAB's floating-point arithmetic
- Rational   Maple's exact symbolic arithmetic
- VPA   Maple's variable-precision arithmetic

For example, the MATLAB statements

```
format long
1/2+1/3
```

use numeric computation to produce

```
0.83333333333333
```

With the Symbolic Math Toolbox, the statement

```
sym(1/2)+1/3
```

uses symbolic computation to yield

```
5/6
```

And, also with the toolbox, the statements

```
digits(25)
vpa('1/2+1/3')
```

use variable-precision arithmetic to return

```
.8333333333333333333333333
```

The floating-point operations used by numeric arithmetic are the fastest of the three, and require the least computer memory, but the results are not exact. The number of digits in the printed output of MATLAB's double quantities is controlled by the format statement, but the internal representation is always the eight-byte floating-point representation provided by the particular computer hardware.

In the computation of the numeric result above, there are actually three roundoff errors, one in the division of 1 by 3, one in the addition of 1/2 to the result of the division, and one in the binary to decimal conversion for the printed output. On computers that use IEEE floating-point standard arithmetic, the resulting internal value is the binary expansion of 5/6, truncated to 53 bits. This is approximately 16 decimal digits. But, in this particular case, the printed output shows only 15 digits.

The symbolic operations used by rational arithmetic are potentially the most expensive of the three, in terms of both computer time and memory. The results are exact, as long as enough time and memory are available to complete the computations.

Variable-precision arithmetic falls in between the other two in terms of both cost and accuracy. A global parameter, set by the function `digits`, controls the number of significant decimal digits. Increasing the number of digits increases the accuracy, but also increases both the time and memory requirements. The default value of `digits` is 32, corresponding roughly to floating-point accuracy.

The Maple documentation uses the term "hardware floating-point" for what we are calling "numeric" or "floating-point" and uses the term "floating-point arithmetic" for what we are calling "variable-precision arithmetic."

Example: Using the Different Kinds of Arithmetic

Rational Arithmetic

By default, the Symbolic Math Toolbox uses rational arithmetic operations, i.e., Maple's exact symbolic arithmetic. Rational arithmetic is invoked when you create symbolic variables using the `sym` function.

The `sym` function converts a double matrix to its symbolic form. For example, if the double matrix is

```
A =
1.1000    1.2000    1.3000
2.1000    2.2000    2.3000
3.1000    3.2000    3.3000
```

its symbolic form, S = sym(A), is

```
S =
[11/10,  6/5, 13/10]
[21/10, 11/5, 23/10]
[31/10, 16/5, 33/10]
```

For this matrix A, it is possible to discover that the elements are the ratios of small integers, so the symbolic representation is formed from those integers. On the other hand, the statement

```
E = [exp(1) sqrt(2); log(3) rand]
```

returns a matrix

```
E =
2.71828182845905    1.41421356237310
1.09861228866811    0.21895918632809
```

whose elements are not the ratios of small integers, so sym(E) reproduces the floating-point representation in a symbolic form.

```
[3060513257434037*2^(-50), 3184525836262886*2^(-51)]
[2473854946935174*2^(-51), 3944418039826132*2^(-54)]
```

Variable-Precision Numbers

Variable-precision numbers are distinguished from the exact rational representation by the presence of a decimal point. A power of 10 scale factor, denoted by 'e', is allowed. To use variable-precision instead of rational arithmetic, create your variables using the vpa function.

For matrices with purely double entries, the vpa function generates the representation that is used with variable-precision arithmetic. Continuing on with our example, and using digits(4), applying vpa to the matrix S

```
vpa(S)
```

generates the output

```
S =
[1.100, 1.200, 1.300]
[2.100, 2.200, 2.300]
[3.100, 3.200, 3.300]
```

and with digits(25)

```
F = vpa(E)
```

generates

```
F =
[2.71828182845904553488480,  1.4142135623730949234300]
[1.09861228866811000415282,   .218959186328089971951271]
```

Converting to Floating-Point

To convert a rational or variable-precision number to its MATLAB floating-point representation, use the double function.

In our example, both double(sym(E)) and double(vpa(E)) return E.

Another Example

The next example is perhaps more interesting. Start with the symbolic expression

```
f = sym('exp(pi*sqrt(163))')
```

The statement

```
double(f)
```

produces the printed floating-point value

```
2.625374126407687e+17
```

Using the second argument of vpa to specify the number of digits,

```
vpa(f,18)
```

returns

```
262537412640768744.
```

whereas

```
vpa(f,25)
```

returns

```
262537412640768744.0000000
```

We suspect that f might actually have an integer value. This suspicion is reinforced by the 30 digit value, vpa(f,30)

```
262537412640768743.999999999999
```

Finally, the 40 digit value, vpa(f,40)

262537412640768743.999999999992500725944

shows that f is very close to, but not exactly equal to, an integer.

Linear Algebra

Basic Algebraic Operations

Basic algebraic operations on symbolic objects are the same as operations on MATLAB objects of class `double`. This is illustrated in the following example.

The Givens transformation produces a plane rotation through the angle `t`. The statements

```
syms t;
G = [cos(t) sin(t); -sin(t) cos(t)]
```

create this transformation matrix.

```
G =
[  cos(t),  sin(t) ]
[ -sin(t),  cos(t) ]
```

Applying the Givens transformation twice should simply be a rotation through twice the angle. The corresponding matrix can be computed by multiplying `G` by itself or by raising `G` to the second power. Both

```
A = G*G
```

and

```
A = G^2
```

produce

```
A =
[cos(t)^2-sin(t)^2,    2*cos(t)*sin(t)]
[ -2*cos(t)*sin(t), cos(t)^2-sin(t)^2]
```

The `simple` function

```
A = simple(A)
```

uses a trigonometric identity to return the expected form by trying several different identities and picking the one that produces the shortest representation.

```
A =
[ cos(2*t), sin(2*t)]
[-sin(2*t), cos(2*t)]
```

A Givens rotation is an orthogonal matrix, so its transpose is its inverse. Confirming this by

```
I = G.' *G
```

which produces

```
I =
[cos(t)^2+sin(t)^2,                 0]
[                0, cos(t)^2+sin(t)^2]
```

and then

```
I = simple(I)
I =
[1, 0]
[0, 1]
```

Linear Algebraic Operations

Let's do several basic linear algebraic operations.

The command

```
H = hilb(3)
```

generates the 3-by-3 Hilbert matrix. With `format short`, MATLAB prints

```
H =
1.0000    0.5000    0.3333
0.5000    0.3333    0.2500
0.3333    0.2500    0.2000
```

The computed elements of H are floating-point numbers that are the ratios of small integers. Indeed, H is a MATLAB array of class double. Converting H to a symbolic matrix

```
H = sym(H)
```

gives

```
[  1, 1/2, 1/3]
[1/2, 1/3, 1/4]
[1/3, 1/4, 1/5]
```

This allows subsequent symbolic operations on H to produce results that correspond to the infinitely precise Hilbert matrix, sym(hilb(3)), not its floating-point approximation, hilb(3). Therefore,

```
inv(H)
```

produces

```
[  9,  -36,   30]
[-36,  192, -180]
[ 30, -180,  180]
```

and

```
det(H)
```

yields

```
1/2160
```

We can use the backslash operator to solve a system of simultaneous linear equations. The commands

```
b = [1 1 1]'
x = H\b    % Solve Hx = b
```

produce the solution

```
[  3]
[-24]
[ 30]
```

All three of these results, the inverse, the determinant, and the solution to the linear system, are the exact results corresponding to the infinitely precise, rational, Hilbert matrix. On the other hand, using digits(16), the command

```
V = vpa(hilb(3))
```

returns

```
[                 1., .5000000000000000, .3333333333333333]
[.5000000000000000, .3333333333333333, .2500000000000000]
[.3333333333333333, .2500000000000000, .2000000000000000]
```

The decimal points in the representation of the individual elements are the signal to use variable-precision arithmetic. The result of each arithmetic operation is rounded to 16 significant decimal digits. When inverting the matrix, these errors are magnified by the matrix condition number, which for hilb(3) is about 500. Consequently,

```
inv(V)
```

which returns

```
[  9.000000000000082,  -36.00000000000039,   30.00000000000035]
[-36.00000000000039,   192.0000000000021,  -180.0000000000019]
[ 30.00000000000035,  -180.0000000000019,   180.0000000000019]
```

shows the loss of two digits. So does

```
det(V)
```

which gives

```
.462962962962958e-3
```

and

```
V\b
```

which is

```
[  3.000000000000041]
[-24.00000000000021]
[ 30.00000000000019]
```

Since H is nonsingular, the null space of H

```
null(H)
```

and the column space of H

```
colspace(H)
```

produce an empty matrix and a permutation of the identity matrix, respectively. To make a more interesting example, let's try to find a value s for H(1,1) that makes H singular. The commands

```
syms s
H(1,1) = s
Z = det(H)
sol = solve(Z)
```

produce

```
H =
[   s, 1/2, 1/3]
[1/2, 1/3, 1/4]
[1/3, 1/4, 1/5]

Z =
1/240*s-1/270

sol =
8/9
```

Then

```
H = subs(H,s,sol)
```

substitutes the computed value of sol for s in H to give

```
H =
[8/9, 1/2, 1/3]
[1/2, 1/3, 1/4]
[1/3, 1/4, 1/5]
```

Now, the command

```
det(H)
```

returns

```
ans =
0
```

and

```
inv(H)
```

produces an error message

```
??? error using ==> inv
Error, (in inverse) singular matrix
```

because H is singular. For this matrix, Z = null(H) and C = colspace(H) are nontrivial.

```
Z =
[    1]
[   -4]
[10/3]

C =
[  0,     1]
[  1,     0]
[6/5, -3/10]
```

It should be pointed out that even though H is singular, vpa(H) is not. For any integer value d, setting

```
digits(d)
```

and then computing

```
det(vpa(H))
inv(vpa(H))
```

results in a determinant of size 10^(-d) and an inverse with elements on the order of 10^d.

Eigenvalues

The symbolic eigenvalues of a square matrix A or the symbolic eigenvalues and eigenvectors of A are computed, respectively, using the commands

```
E = eig(A)
[V,E] = eig(A)
```

The variable-precision counterparts are

```
E = eig(vpa(A))
[V,E] = eig(vpa(A))
```

The eigenvalues of A are the zeros of the characteristic polynomial of A, det(A-x*I), which is computed by

```
poly(A)
```

The matrix H from the last section provides our first example.

```
H =
[8/9, 1/2, 1/3]
[1/2, 1/3, 1/4]
[1/3, 1/4, 1/5]
```

The matrix is singular, so one of its eigenvalues must be zero. The statement

```
[T,E] = eig(H)
```

produces the matrices T and E. The columns of T are the eigenvectors of H.

```
T =

[    1, 28/153+2/153*12589^(1/2),  28/153-2/153*12589^(12)]
[   -4,                        1,                        1]
[ 10/3, 92/255-1/255*12589^(1/2), 292/255+1/255*12589^(12)]
```

Similarly, the diagonal elements of E are the eigenvalues of H.

```
E =

[0,                        0,                              0]
[0, 32/45+1/180*12589^(1/2),                              0]
[0,                        0, 32/45-1/180*12589^(1/2)]
```

It may be easier to understand the structure of the matrices of eigenvectors, T, and eigenvalues, E, if we convert T and E to decimal notation. We proceed as follows. The commands

```
Td = double(T)
Ed = double(E)
```

```
return
Td =
    1.0000    1.6497   -1.2837
   -4.0000    1.0000    1.0000
    3.3333    0.7051    1.5851
Ed =
    0         0         0
    0    1.3344         0
    0         0    0.0878
```

The first eigenvalue is zero. The corresponding eigenvector (the first column of Td) is the same as the basis for the null space found in the last section. The other two eigenvalues are the result of applying the quadratic formula to

```
x^2-64/45*x+253/2160
```

which is the quadratic factor in factor(poly(H)).

```
syms x
g = simple(factor(poly(H))/x);
solve(g)
```

Closed form symbolic expressions for the eigenvalues are possible only when the characteristic polynomial can be expressed as a product of rational polynomials of degree four or less. The Rosser matrix is a classic numerical analysis test matrix that happens to illustrate this requirement. The statement

```
R = sym(gallery('rosser'))
```

generates

```
R =
[  611    196   -192    407     -8    -52    -49     29]
[  196    899    113   -192    -71    -43     -8    -44]
[ -192    113    899    196     61     49      8     52]
[  407   -192    196    611      8     44     59    -23]
[   -8    -71     61      8    411   -599    208    208]
[  -52    -43     49     44   -599    411    208    208]
[  -49     -8      8     59    208    208     99   -911]
[   29    -44     52    -23    208    208   -911     99]
```

The commands

```
p = poly(R);
pretty(factor(p))
```

produce

$$x \ (x \ - \ 1020) \ (x^2 \ - \ 1020 \ x \ + \ 100) (x^2 \ - \ 1040500) \ (x \ - \ 1000)^2$$

The characteristic polynomial (of degree 8) factors nicely into the product of two linear terms and three quadratic terms. We can see immediately that four of the eigenvalues are 0, 1020, and a double root at 1000. The other four roots are obtained from the remaining quadratics. Use

```
eig(R)
```

to find all these values

```
[               0]
[            1020]
[510+100*26^(1/2)]
[510-100*26^(1/2)]
[   10*10405^(1/2)]
[  -10*10405^(1/2)]
[            1000]
[            1000]
```

The Rosser matrix is not a typical example; it is rare for a full 8-by-8 matrix to have a characteristic polynomial that factors into such simple form. If we change the two "corner" elements of R from 29 to 30 with the commands

```
S = R;   S(1,8) = 30;   S(8,1) = 30;
```

and then try

```
p = poly(S)
```

we find

```
p =
40250968213600000+51264008540948000*x-
    1082699388411166000*x^2+4287832912719760*x^-3-
    5327831918568*x^4+82706090*x^5+5079941*x^6-
    4040*x^7+x^8
```

We also find that `factor(p)` is p itself. That is, the characteristic polynomial cannot be factored over the rationals.

For this modified Rosser matrix

```
F = eig(S)
```

returns

```
F =
[  -1020.0532142558915165931894252600]
[  -.17053529728768998575200874607757]
[   .21803980548301606860857564424981]
[   999.94691786044276755320289228602]
[   1000.1206982933841335712817075454]
[   1019.5243552632016358324933278291]
[   1019.9935501291629257348091808173]
[   1020.4201882015047278185457498840]
```

Notice that these values are close to the eigenvalues of the original Rosser matrix. Further, the numerical values of F are a result of Maple's floating-point arithmetic. Consequently, different settings of `digits` do not alter the number of digits to the right of the decimal place.

It is also possible to try to compute eigenvalues of symbolic matrices, but closed form solutions are rare. The Givens transformation is generated as the matrix exponential of the elementary matrix

$$A = \begin{bmatrix} 0 & 1 \\ -1 & 0 \end{bmatrix}$$

The Symbolic Math Toolbox commands

```
syms t
A = sym([0 1; -1 0]);
G = expm(t*A)
```

return

```
[  cos(t),  sin(t)]
[ -sin(t),  cos(t)]
```

Next, the command

```
g = eig(G)
```

produces

```
g =
[ cos(t)+(cos(t)^2-1)^(1/2)]
[ cos(t)-(cos(t)^2-1)^(1/2)]
```

We can use simple to simplify this form of g. Indeed, repeated application of simple

```
for  j = 1:4
    [g,how] = simple(g)
end
```

produces the best result

```
g =
[ cos(t)+(-sin(t)^2)^(1/2)]
[ cos(t)-(-sin(t)^2)^(1/2)]

how =
simplify

g =
[ cos(t)+i*sin(t)]
[ cos(t)-i*sin(t)]

how =
radsimp

g =
[    exp(i*t)]
[ 1/exp(i*t)]

how =
convert(exp)

g =
[    exp(i*t)]
[ exp(-i*t)]
```

```
how =
combine
```

Notice the first application of `simple` uses `simplify` to produce a sum of sines and cosines. Next, `simple` invokes `radsimp` to produce `cos(t) + i*sin(t)` for the first eigenvector. The third application of `simple` uses `convert(exp)` to change the sines and cosines to complex exponentials. The last application of `simple` uses `simplify` to obtain the final form.

Jordan Canonical Form

The Jordan canonical form results from attempts to diagonalize a matrix by a similarity transformation. For a given matrix A, find a nonsingular matrix V, so that `inv(V)*A*V`, or, more succinctly, `J = V\A*V`, is "as close to diagonal as possible." For almost all matrices, the Jordan canonical form is the diagonal matrix of eigenvalues and the columns of the transformation matrix are the eigenvectors. This always happens if the matrix is symmetric or if it has distinct eigenvalues. Some nonsymmetric matrices with multiple eigenvalues cannot be diagonalized. The Jordan form has the eigenvalues on its diagonal, but some of the superdiagonal elements are one, instead of zero. The statement

```
J = jordan(A)
```

computes the Jordan canonical form of A. The statement

```
[V,J] = jordan(A)
```

also computes the similarity transformation. The columns of V are the generalized eigenvectors of A.

The Jordan form is extremely sensitive to perturbations. Almost any change in A causes its Jordan form to be diagonal. This makes it very difficult to compute the Jordan form reliably with floating-point arithmetic. It also implies that A must be known exactly (i.e., without round-off error, etc.). Its elements must be integers, or ratios of small integers. In particular, the variable-precision calculation, `jordan(vpa(A))`, is not allowed.

For example, let

```
A = sym([12,32,66,116;-25,-76,-164,-294;
        21,66,143,256;-6,-19,-41,-73])
A =
[   12,    32,    66,    116]
[  -25,   -76,  -164,   -294]
[   21,    66,   143,    256]
[   -6,   -19,   -41,    -73]
```

Then

```
[V,J] = jordan(A)
```

produces

```
V =
[    4,    -2,     4,     3]
[   -6,     8,   -11,    -8]
[    4,    -7,    10,     7]
[   -1,     2,    -3,    -2]

J =
[ 1, 1, 0, 0]
[ 0, 1, 0, 0]
[ 0, 0, 2, 1]
[ 0, 0, 0, 2]
```

Therefore A has a double eigenvalue at 1, with a single Jordan block, and a double eigenvalue at 2, also with a single Jordan block. The matrix has only two eigenvectors, V(:,1) and V(:,3). They satisfy

```
A*V(:,1) = 1*V(:,1)
A*V(:,3) = 2*V(:,3)
```

The other two columns of V are generalized eigenvectors of grade 2. They satisfy

```
A*V(:,2) = 1*V(:,2) + V(:,1)
A*V(:,4) = 2*V(:,4) + V(:,3)
```

In mathematical notation, with $\mathbf{v}_j = v(:,j)$, the columns of V and eigenvalues satisfy the relationships

$$(A - \lambda_2 I)v_4 = v_3$$

$$(A - \lambda_1 I)v_2 = v_1$$

Singular Value Decomposition

Only the variable-precision numeric computation of the singular value decomposition is available in the toolbox. One reason for this is that the formulas that result from symbolic computation are usually too long and complicated to be of much use. If A is a symbolic matrix of floating-point or variable-precision numbers, then

```
S = svd(A)
```

computes the singular values of A to an accuracy determined by the current setting of digits. And

```
[U,S,V] = svd(A);
```

produces two orthogonal matrices, U and V, and a diagonal matrix, S, so that

```
A = U*S*V';
```

Let's look at the n-by-n matrix A with elements defined by

```
A(i,j) = 1/(i-j+1/2)
```

For n = 5, the matrix is

```
[  2     -2    -2/3   -2/5    -2/7]
[2/3      2    -2     -2/3    -2/5]
[2/5    2/3     2     -2      -2/3]
[2/7    2/5   2/3      2       -2]
[2/9    2/7   2/5     2/3       2]
```

It turns out many of the singular values of these matrices are close to π.

The most obvious way of generating this matrix is

```
for i=1:n
    for j=1:n
        A(i,j) = sym(1/(i-j+1/2));
    end
end
```

The most efficient way to generate the matrix is

```
[J,I] = meshgrid(1:n);
A = sym(1./(I - J+1/2));
```

Since the elements of A are the ratios of small integers, vpa(A) produces a variable-precision representation, which is accurate to digits precision. Hence

```
S = svd(vpa(A))
```

computes the desired singular values to full accuracy. With n = 16 and digits(30), the result is

```
S =
[ 1.2096813760566898985332455685357 ]
[ 2.6916215868606660677482763594 ]
[ 3.0779029723111974865842472735 ]
[ 3.1350405439974465484389890126 ]
[ 3.1410604466347006380521837192 ]
[ 3.1415575435991808369105065826 ]
[ 3.1415907545860584872898257711 ]
[ 3.1415925692549230647028486310 ]
[ 3.1415926505265488081556947961 ]
[ 3.1415926534996105314385683856 ]
[ 3.1415926535876736171239261238 ]
[ 3.1415926535897543920684990722 ]
[ 3.1415926535897927034263555905 ]
[ 3.1415926535897932332529014278 ]
[ 3.1415926535897932384306684671 ]
[ 3.1415926535897932384625503597 ]
```

There are two ways to compare S with pi, the floating-point representation of π. In the vector below, the first element is computed by subtraction with variable-precision arithmetic and then converted to a double. The second element is computed with floating-point arithmetic.

```
format short e
[double(pi*ones(16,1)-S)  pi-double(S)]
```

The results are

1.9319e+00	1.9319e+00
4.4997e-01	4.4997e-01
6.3690e-02	6.3690e-02
6.5521e-03	6.5521e-03
5.3221e-04	5.3221e-04
3.5110e-05	3.5110e-05
1.8990e-06	1.8990e-06
8.4335e-08	8.4335e-08
3.0632e-09	3.0632e-09
9.0183e-11	9.0183e-11
2.1196e-12	2.1196e-12
3.8846e-14	3.8636e-14
5.3504e-16	4.4409e-16
5.2097e-18	0
3.1975e-20	0
9.3024e-23	0

Since the relative accuracy of pi is pi*eps, which is 6.9757e-16, either column confirms our suspicion that four of the singular values of the 16-by-16 example equal π to floating-point accuracy.

Eigenvalue Trajectories

This example applies several numeric, symbolic, and graphic techniques to study the behavior of matrix eigenvalues as a parameter in the matrix is varied. This particular setting involves numerical analysis and perturbation theory, but the techniques illustrated are more widely applicable.

In this example, we consider a 3-by-3 matrix A whose eigenvalues are 1, 2, 3. First, we perturb A by another matrix E and parameter $t: A \rightarrow A + tE$. As t

increases from 0 to 10^{-6}, the eigenvalues $\lambda_1 = 1$, $\lambda_2 = 2$, $\lambda_3 = 3$ change to $\lambda_1' \approx 1.5596 + 0.2726i$, $\lambda_2' \approx 1.5596 - 0.2726i$, $\lambda_3' \approx 2.8808$.

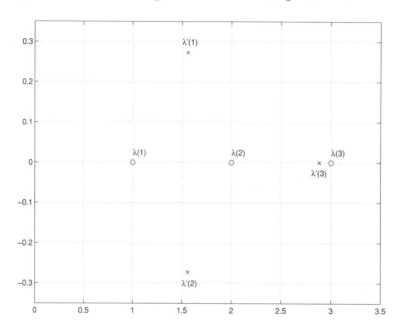

This, in turn, means that for some value of $t = \tau$, $0 < \tau < 10^{-6}$, the perturbed matrix $A(t) = A + tE$ has a double eigenvalue $\lambda_1 = \lambda_2$.

Let's find the value of t, called τ, where this happens.

The starting point is a MATLAB test example, known as gallery(3).

```
A = gallery(3)
A =
    -149      -50     -154
     537      180      546
     -27       -9      -25
```

This is an example of a matrix whose eigenvalues are sensitive to the effects of roundoff errors introduced during their computation. The actual computed eigenvalues may vary from one machine to another, but on a typical workstation, the statements

```
format long
e = eig(A)
```

produce

```
e =
    0.99999999999642
    2.00000000000579
    2.99999999999780
```

Of course, the example was created so that its eigenvalues are actually 1, 2, and 3. Note that three or four digits have been lost to roundoff. This can be easily verified with the toolbox. The statements

```
B = sym(A);
e = eig(B)'
p = poly(B)
f = factor(p)
```

produce

```
e =
[1,   2,   3]

p =
x^3-6*x^2+11*x-6

f =
(x-1)*(x-2)*(x-3)
```

Are the eigenvalues sensitive to the perturbations caused by roundoff error because they are "close together"? Ordinarily, the values 1, 2, and 3 would be regarded as "well separated." But, in this case, the separation should be viewed on the scale of the original matrix. If A were replaced by A/1000, the eigenvalues, which would be .001, .002, .003, would "seem" to be closer together.

But eigenvalue sensitivity is more subtle than just "closeness." With a carefully chosen perturbation of the matrix, it is possible to make two of its eigenvalues coalesce into an actual double root that is extremely sensitive to roundoff and other errors.

One good perturbation direction can be obtained from the outer product of the left and right eigenvectors associated with the most sensitive eigenvalue. The following statement creates

```
E = [130,-390,0;43,-129,0;133,-399,0]
```

the perturbation matrix

```
E =
130   -390      0
 43   -129      0
133   -399      0
```

The perturbation can now be expressed in terms of a single, scalar parameter t. The statements

```
syms x t
A = A+t*E
```

replace A with the symbolic representation of its perturbation.

```
A =
[-149+130*t,  -50-390*t,  -154]
[  537+43*t,  180-129*t,   546]
[  -27+133*t,   -9-399*t,   -25]
```

Computing the characteristic polynomial of this new A

```
p = poly(A)
```

gives

```
p =
x^3-6*x^2+11*x-t*x^2+492512*t*x-6-1221271*t
```

Prettyprinting

```
pretty(collect(p,x))
```

shows more clearly that p is a cubic in x whose coefficients vary linearly with t.

```
     3              2
    x  + (- t - 6) x  + (492512 t + 11) x - 6 - 1221271 t
```

It turns out that when t is varied over a very small interval, from 0 to 1.0e-6, the desired double root appears. This can best be seen graphically. The first figure shows plots of p, considered as a function of x, for three different values of t: t = 0, t = 0.5e-6, and t = 1.0e-6. For each value, the eigenvalues are computed numerically and also plotted.

```
x = .8:.01:3.2;
for k = 0:2
  c = sym2poly(subs(p,t,k*0.5e-6));
  y = polyval(c,x);
  lambda = eig(double(subs(A,t,k*0.5e-6)));
  subplot(3,1,3-k)
  plot(x,y,'-',x,0*x,':',lambda,0*lambda,'o')
  axis([.8 3.2 -.5 .5])
  text(2.25,.35,['t = ' num2str( k*0.5e-6 )]);
end
```

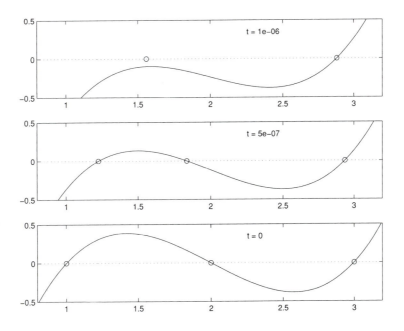

The bottom subplot shows the unperturbed polynomial, with its three roots at 1, 2, and 3. The middle subplot shows the first two roots approaching each other. In the top subplot, these two roots have become complex and only one real root remains.

The next statements compute and display the actual eigenvalues

```
e = eig(A);
pretty(e)
```

showing that e(2) and e(3) form a complex conjugate pair.

```
[                                    1/3                                      ]
[                        1/3 %1      - 3 %2 + 2 + 1/3 t                        ]
[                                                                             ]
[            1/3                              1/2        1/3                   ]
[- 1/6 %1      + 3/2 %2 + 2 + 1/3 t + 1/2 i 3    (1/3 %1     + 3 %2)]
[                                                                             ]
[            1/3                              1/2        1/3                   ]
[- 1/6 %1      + 3/2 %2 + 2 + 1/3 t - 1/2 i 3    (1/3 %1     + 3 %2)]

                                  2     3
%1 := 3189393 t - 2216286 t  + t  + 3 (-3 + 4432572 t

                   2                          3
     - 1052829647418 t + 358392752910068940 t

                   4 1/2
     - 181922388795 t )

                                      2
          - 1/3 + 492508/3 t - 1/9 t
%2 := ---------------------------
                   1/3
                 %1
```

Next, the symbolic representations of the three eigenvalues are evaluated at many values of t

```
tvals = (2:-.02:0)' * 1.e-6;
r = size(tvals,1);
c = size(e,1);
lambda = zeros(r,c);
for k = 1:c
   lambda(:,k) = double(subs(e(k),t,tvals));
end
plot(lambda,tvals)
xlabel('\lambda'); ylabel('t');
title('Eigenvalue Transition')
```

to produce a plot of their trajectories.

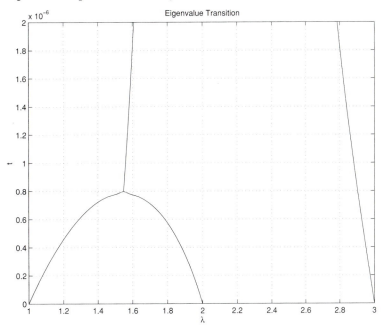

Above $t = 0.8e^{-6}$, the graphs of two of the eigenvalues intersect, while below $t = 0.8e^{-6}$, two real roots become a complex conjugate pair. What is the precise value of t that marks this transition? Let τ denote this value of t.

One way to find τ is based on the fact that, at a double root, both the function and its derivative must vanish. This results in two polynomial equations to be solved for two unknowns. The statement

```
sol = solve(p,diff(p,'x'))
```

solves the pair of algebraic equations p = 0 and dp/dx = 0 and produces

```
sol =
    t: [4x1 sym]
    x: [4x1 sym]
```

Find τ now by

```
tau = double(sol.t(2))
```

which reveals that the second element of sol.t is the desired value of τ.

```
format short
tau =
   7.8379e-07
```

Therefore, the second element of sol.x

```
sigma = double(sol.x(2))
```

is the double eigenvalue

```
sigma =
   1.5476
```

Let's verify that this value of τ does indeed produce a double eigenvalue at σ = 1.5476. To achieve this, substitute τ for t in the perturbed matrix $A(t) = A + tE$ and find the eigenvalues of $A(t)$. That is,

```
e = eig(double(subs(A,t,tau)))

e =

    1.5476
    1.5476
    2.9047
```

confirms that σ = 1.5476 is a double eigenvalue of $A(t)$ for t = 7.8379e-07.

Solving Equations

Solving Algebraic Equations

If S is a symbolic expression,

```
solve(S)
```

attempts to find values of the symbolic variable in S (as determined by findsym) for which S is zero. For example,

```
syms a b c x
S = a*x^2 + b*x + c;
solve(S)
```

uses the familiar quadratic formula to produce

```
ans =
[1/2/a*(-b+(b^2-4*a*c)^(1/2))]
[1/2/a*(-b-(b^2-4*a*c)^(1/2))]
```

This is a symbolic vector whose elements are the two solutions.

If you want to solve for a specific variable, you must specify that variable as an additional argument. For example, if you want to solve S for b, use the command

```
b = solve(S,b)
```

which returns

```
b =
-(a*x^2+c)/x
```

Note that these examples assume equations of the form $f(x) = 0$. If you need to solve equations of the form $f(x) = q(x)$, you must use quoted strings. In particular, the command

```
s = solve('cos(2*x)+sin(x)=1')
```

returns a vector with four solutions.

```
s =
[       0]
[      pi]
[ 1/6*pi]
[ 5/6*pi]
```

Several Algebraic Equations

Now let's look at systems of equations. Suppose we have the system

$$x^2 y^2 = 0$$

$$x - \frac{y}{2} = \alpha$$

and we want to solve for x and y. First create the necessary symbolic objects.

```
syms x y alpha
```

There are several ways to address the output of solve. One is to use a two-output call

```
[x,y] = solve(x^2*y^2, x-y/2-alpha)
```

which returns

```
x =
[     0]
[     0]
[ alpha]
[ alpha]

y =
[ -2*alpha]
[ -2*alpha]
[        0]
[        0]
```

Consequently, the solution vector

```
v = [x, y]
```

appears to have redundant components. This is due to the first equation $x^2 y^2 = 0$, which has two solutions in x and y: $x = \pm 0$, $y = \pm 0$. Changing the equations to

```
eqs1 = 'x^2*y^2=1, x-y/2-alpha'
[x,y] = solve(eqs1)
```

produces four distinct solutions.

```
x =
[ 1/2*alpha+1/2*(alpha^2+2)^(1/2)]
[ 1/2*alpha-1/2*(alpha^2+2)^(1/2)]
[ 1/2*alpha+1/2*(alpha^2-2)^(1/2)]
[ 1/2*alpha-1/2*(alpha^2-2)^(1/2)]


y =
[ -alpha+(alpha^2+2)^(1/2)]
[ -alpha-(alpha^2+2)^(1/2)]
[ -alpha+(alpha^2-2)^(1/2)]
[ -alpha-(alpha^2-2)^(1/2)]
```

Since we did not specify the dependent variables, solve uses findsym to determine the variables.

This way of assigning output from solve is quite successful for "small" systems. Plainly, if we had, say, a 10-by-10 system of equations, typing

```
[x1,x2,x3,x4,x5,x6,x7,x8,x9,x10] = solve(...)
```

is both awkward and time consuming. To circumvent this difficulty, solve can return a structure whose fields are the solutions. In particular, consider the system u^2-v^2 = a^2, u + v = 1, a^2-2*a = 3. The command

```
S = solve('u^2-v^2 = a^2','u + v = 1','a^2-2*a = 3')
```

returns

```
S =
    a: [2x1 sym]
    u: [2x1 sym]
    v: [2x1 sym]
```

The solutions for a reside in the "a-field" of S. That is,

```
S.a
```

produces

```
ans =
[ -1]
[  3]
```

Similar comments apply to the solutions for u and v. The structure S can now be manipulated by field and index to access a particular portion of the solution. For example, if we want to examine the second solution, we can use the following statement

```
s2 = [S.a(2), S.u(2), S.v(2)]
```

to extract the second component of each field.

```
s2 =
[  3,   5,  -4]
```

The following statement

```
M = [S.a, S.u, S.v]
```

creates the solution matrix M

```
M =
[ -1,   1,   0]
[  3,   5,  -4]
```

whose rows comprise the distinct solutions of the system.

Linear systems of simultaneous equations can also be solved using matrix division. For example,

```
clear u v x y
syms u v x y
S = solve(x+2*y-u, 4*x+5*y-v);
sol = [S.x;S.y]
```

and

```
A = [1 2; 4 5];
b = [u; v];
z = A\b
```

result in

```
sol =

[  -5/3*u+2/3*v]
[   4/3*u-1/3*v]

z =
[  -5/3*u+2/3*v]
[   4/3*u-1/3*v]
```

Thus s and z produce the same solution, although the results are assigned to different variables.

Single Differential Equation

The function dsolve computes symbolic solutions to ordinary differential equations. The equations are specified by symbolic expressions containing the letter D to denote differentiation. The symbols D2, D3, ... DN, correspond to the second, third, ..., Nth derivative, respectively. Thus, D2y is the Symbolic Math Toolbox equivalent of d^2y/dt^2. The dependent variables are those preceded by D and the default independent variable is t. Note that names of symbolic variables should not contain D. The independent variable can be changed from t to some other symbolic variable by including that variable as the last input argument.

Initial conditions can be specified by additional equations. If initial conditions are not specified, the solutions contain constants of integration, C1, C2, etc.

The output from dsolve parallels the output from solve. That is, you can call dsolve with the number of output variables equal to the number of dependent variables or place the output in a structure whose fields contain the solutions of the differential equations.

Example 1

The following call to dsolve

```
dsolve('Dy=1+y^2')
```

uses y as the dependent variable and t as the default independent variable. The output of this command is

```
ans =
tan(t+C1)
```

To specify an initial condition, use

```
y = dsolve('Dy=1+y^2','y(0)=1')
```

This produces

```
y =
tan(t+1/4*pi)
```

Notice that y is in the MATLAB workspace, but the independent variable t is not. Thus, the command diff(y,t) returns an error. To place t in the workspace, type syms t.

Example 2

Nonlinear equations may have multiple solutions, even when initial conditions are given.

```
x = dsolve('(Dx)^2+x^2=1','x(0)=0')
```

results in

```
x =
[-sin(t)]
[ sin(t)]
```

Example 3

Here is a second order differential equation with two initial conditions. The commands

```
y = dsolve('D2y=cos(2*x)-y','y(0)=1','Dy(0)=0', 'x')
simplify(y)
```

produce

```
y =
-2/3*cos(x)^2+1/3+4/3*cos(x)
```

The key issues in this example are the order of the equation and the initial conditions. To solve the ordinary differential equation

$$\frac{d^3u}{dx^3} = u$$

$u(0) = 1, u'(0) = -1, u''(0) = \pi$

simply type

```
u = dsolve('D3u=u','u(0)=1','Du(0)=-1','D2u(0) = pi','x')
```

Use D3u to represent d^3u/dx^3 and D2u(0) for $u''(0)$.

Several Differential Equations

The function dsolve can also handle several ordinary differential equations in several variables, with or without initial conditions. For example, here is a pair of linear, first order equations.

```
S = dsolve('Df = 3*f+4*g', 'Dg = -4*f+3*g')
```

The computed solutions are returned in the structure S. You can determine the values of f and g by typing

```
f = S.f
f =
C2*exp(3*t)*sin(4*t)-C1*exp(3*t)*cos(4*t)

g = S.g
g =
C1*exp(3*t)*sin(4*t)+C2*exp(3*t)*cos(4*t)
```

If you prefer to recover f and g directly as well as include initial conditions, type

```
[f,g] = dsolve('Df=3*f+4*g, Dg =-4*f+3*g', 'f(0) = 0, g(0) = 1')

f =
exp(3*t)*sin(4*t)


g =
exp(3*t)*cos(4*t)
```

This table details some examples and Symbolic Math Toolbox syntax. Note that the final entry in the table is the Airy differential equation whose solution is referred to as the Airy function.

Differential Equation	MATLAB Command
$\dfrac{dy}{dt} + 4y(t) = e^{-t}$ $y(0) = 1$	```y = dsolve('Dy+4*y = exp(-t)', 'y(0) = 1')```
$\dfrac{d^2 y}{dx^2} + 4y(x) = e^{-2x}$ $y(0) = 0, y(\pi) = 0$	```y = dsolve('D2y+4*y = exp(-2*x)', 'y(0)=0', 'y(pi) = 0', 'x')```
$\dfrac{d^2 y}{dx^2} = xy(x)$ $y(0) = 0, y(3) = \dfrac{1}{\pi}K_{\frac{1}{3}}(2\sqrt{3})$ (The Airy Equation)	```y = dsolve('D2y = x*y','y(0) = 0', 'y(3) = besselk(1/3, 2*sqrt(3))/pi', 'x')```

The Airy function plays an important role in the mathematical modeling of the dispersion of water waves.

A

MATLAB Quick Reference

Introduction

This appendix lists the MATLAB functions as they are grouped in the Help Desk by subject. Each table contains the function names and brief descriptions. For complete information about any of these functions, refer to the Help Desk and either:

- Select the function from the MATLAB Functions list (By Subject or By Index), or
- Type the function name in the **Go to MATLAB function** field and click **Go**.

Note If you are viewing this book from the Help Desk, you can click on any function name and jump directly to the corresponding MATLAB function page.

General Purpose Commands

This set of functions lets you start and stop MATLAB, work with files and the operating system, control the command window, and manage the environment, variables, and the workspace.

Managing Commands and Functions

addpath	Add directories to MATLAB's search path
doc	Display HTML documentation in Web browser
docopt	Display location of help file directory for UNIX platforms
help	Online help for MATLAB functions and M-files
helpdesk	Display Help Desk page in Web browser, giving access to extensive help
helpwin	Display Help Window, providing access to help for all commands
lasterr	Last error message
lastwarn	Last warning message
lookfor	Keyword search through all help entries
partialpath	Partial pathname
path	Control MATLAB's directory search path
pathtool	Start Path Browser, a GUI for viewing and modifying MATLAB's path
profile	Start the M-file profiler, a utility for debugging and optimizing code
profreport	Generate a profile report
rmpath	Remove directories from MATLAB's search path
type	List file

Managing Commands and Functions (Continued)

ver	Display version information for MATLAB, Simulink, and toolboxes
version	MATLAB version number
web	Point Web browser at file or Web site
what	Directory listing of M-files, MAT-files, and MEX-files
whatsnew	Display README files for MATLAB and toolboxes
which	Locate functions and files

Managing Variables and the Workspace

clear	Remove items from memory
disp	Display text or array
length	Length of vector
load	Retrieve variables from disk
mlock	Prevent M-file clearing
munlock	Allow M-file clearing
openvar	Open workspace variable in Array Editor for graphical editing
pack	Consolidate workspace memory
save	Save workspace variables on disk
saveas	Save figure or model using specified format
size	Array dimensions
who, whos	List directory of variables in memory
workspace	Display the Workspace Browser, a GUI for managing the workspace

Controlling the Command Window

clc	Clear command window
echo	Echo M-files during execution
format	Control the output display format
home	Move the cursor to the home position
more	Control paged output for the command window

Working with Files and the Operating Environment

cd	Change working directory
copyfile	Copy file
delete	Delete files and graphics objects
diary	Save session in a disk file
dir	Directory listing
edit	Edit an M-file
fileparts	Filename parts
fullfile	Build full filename from parts
inmem	Functions in memory
ls	List directory on UNIX
matlabroot	Root directory of MATLAB installation
mkdir	Make directory
open	Open files based on extension
pwd	Display current directory
tempdir	Return the name of the system's temporary directory
tempname	Unique name for temporary file
!	Execute operating system command

Starting and Quitting MATLAB

matlabrc	MATLAB startup M-file
quit	Terminate MATLAB
startup	MATLAB startup M-file

Operators and Special Characters

These are the actual operators you use to enter and manipulate data, for example, matrix multiplication, array multiplication, and line continuation.

Operators and Special Characters

+	Plus
-	Minus
*	Matrix multiplication
.*	Array multiplication
^	Matrix power
.^	Array power
kron	Kronecker tensor product
\	Backslash or left division
/	Slash or right division
./ and .\	Array division, right and left
:	Colon
( )	Parentheses
[ ]	Brackets
{}	Curly braces
.	Decimal point
...	Continuation
,	Comma
;	Semicolon
%	Comment
!	Exclamation point
'	Transpose and quote
.'	Nonconjugated transpose
=	Assignment

Operators and Special Characters (Continued)

==	Equality
< >	Relational operators
&	Logical and
|	Logical or
~	Logical not
xor	Logical exclusive or

Logical Functions

This set of functions performs logical operations such as checking if a file or variable exists and testing if all elements in an array are nonzero. "Operators and Special Characters" contains other operators that perform logical operations.

Logical Functions

all	Test to determine if all elements are nonzero
any	Test for any nonzeros
exist	Check if a variable or file exists
find	Find indices and values of nonzero elements
is*	Detect state
isa	Detect an object of a given class
logical	Convert numeric values to logical
mislocked	True if M-file cannot be cleared

Language Constructs and Debugging

These functions let you work with MATLAB as a programming language. For example, you can control program flow, define global variables, perform interactive input, and debug your code.

MATLAB as a Programming Language

builtin	Execute builtin function from overloaded method
eval	Interpret strings containing MATLAB expressions
evalc	Evaluate MATLAB expression with capture
evalin	Evaluate expression in workspace
feval	Function evaluation
function	Function M-files
global	Define global variables
nargchk	Check number of input arguments
persistent	Define persistent variable
script	Script M-files

Control Flow

break	Terminate execution of for loop or while loop
case	Case switch
catch	Begin catch block
else	Conditionally execute statements
elseif	Conditionally execute statements
end	Terminate for, while, switch, try, and if statements or indicate last
error	Display error messages
for	Repeat statements a specific number of times
if	Conditionally execute statements
otherwise	Default part of switch statement
return	Return to the invoking function

Control Flow (Continued)

switch	Switch among several cases based on expression
try	Begin try block
warning	Display warning message
while	Repeat statements an indefinite number of times

Interactive Input

input	Request user input
keyboard	Invoke the keyboard in an M-file
menu	Generate a menu of choices for user input
pause	Halt execution temporarily

Object-Oriented Programming

class	Create object or return class of object
double	Convert to double precision
inferiorto	Inferior class relationship
inline	Construct an inline object
int8, int16, int32	Convert to signed integer
isa	Detect an object of a given class
loadobj	Extends the load function for user objects
saveobj	Save filter for objects
single	Convert to single precision
superiorto	Superior class relationship
uint8, uint16, uint32	Convert to unsigned integer

Debugging

dbclear	Clear breakpoints
dbcont	Resume execution
dbdown	Change local workspace context
dbmex	Enable MEX-file debugging
dbquit	Quit debug mode

Debugging (Continued)

dbstack	Display function call stack
dbstatus	List all breakpoints
dbstep	Execute one or more lines from a breakpoint
dbstop	Set breakpoints in an M-file function
dbtype	List M-file with line numbers
dbup	Change local workspace context

Elementary Matrices and Matrix Manipulation

Using these functions you can manipulate matrices, and access time, date, special variables, and constants, functions.

Elementary Matrices and Arrays

blkdiag	Construct a block diagonal matrix from input arguments
eye	Identity matrix
linspace	Generate linearly spaced vectors
logspace	Generate logarithmically spaced vectors
ones	Create an array of all ones
rand	Uniformly distributed random numbers and arrays
randn	Normally distributed random numbers and arrays
zeros	Create an array of all zeros
: (colon)	Regularly spaced vector

Special Variables and Constants

ans	The most recent answer
computer	Identify the computer on which MATLAB is running
eps	Floating-point relative accuracy
flops	Count floating-point operations
i	Imaginary unit

Special Variables and Constants (Continued)

Inf	Infinity
inputname	Input argument name
j	Imaginary unit
NaN	Not-a-Number
nargin, nargout	Number of function arguments
pi	Ratio of a circle's circumference to its diameter,
realmax	Largest positive floating-point number
realmin	Smallest positive floating-point number
varargin, varargout	Pass or return variable numbers of arguments

Time and Dates

calendar	Calendar
clock	Current time as a date vector
cputime	Elapsed CPU time
date	Current date string
datenum	Serial date number
datestr	Date string format
datevec	Date components
eomday	End of month
etime	Elapsed time
now	Current date and time
tic, toc	Stopwatch timer
weekday	Day of the week

Matrix Manipulation

cat	Concatenate arrays
diag	Diagonal matrices and diagonals of a matrix
fliplr	Flip matrices left-right
flipud	Flip matrices up-down
repmat	Replicate and tile an array
reshape	Reshape array

Matrix Manipulation (Continued)

rot90	Rotate matrix 90 degrees
tril	Lower triangular part of a matrix
triu	Upper triangular part of a matrix
: (colon)	Index into array, rearrange array

Specialized Matrices

These functions let you work with matrices such as Hadamard, Hankel, Hilbert, and magic squares.

Specialized Matrices

compan	Companion matrix
gallery	Test matrices
hadamard	Hadamard matrix
hankel	Hankel matrix
hilb	Hilbert matrix
invhilb	Inverse of the Hilbert matrix
magic	Magic square
pascal	Pascal matrix
toeplitz	Toeplitz matrix
wilkinson	Wilkinson's eigenvalue test matrix

Elementary Math Functions

These are many of the standard mathematical functions such as trigonometric, hyperbolic, logarithmic, and complex number manipulation.

Elementary Math Functions

abs	Absolute value and complex magnitude
acos, acosh	Inverse cosine and inverse hyperbolic cosine

A-7

Elementary Math Functions (Continued)

`acot, acoth`	Inverse cotangent and inverse hyperbolic cotangent
`acsc, acsch`	Inverse cosecant and inverse hyperbolic cosecant
`angle`	Phase angle
`asec, asech`	Inverse secant and inverse hyperbolic secant
`asin, asinh`	Inverse sine and inverse hyperbolic sine
`atan, atanh`	Inverse tangent and inverse hyperbolic tangent
`atan2`	Four-quadrant inverse tangent
`ceil`	Round toward infinity
`complex`	Construct complex data from real and imaginary components
`conj`	Complex conjugate
`cos, cosh`	Cosine and hyperbolic cosine
`cot, coth`	Cotangent and hyperbolic cotangent
`csc, csch`	Cosecant and hyperbolic cosecant
`exp`	Exponential
`fix`	Round towards zero
`floor`	Round towards minus infinity
`gcd`	Greatest common divisor
`imag`	Imaginary part of a complex number
`lcm`	Least common multiple
`log`	Natural logarithm
`log2`	Base 2 logarithm and dissect floating-point numbers into exponent and
`log10`	Common (base 10) logarithm
`mod`	Modulus (signed remainder after division)
`nchoosek`	Binomial coefficient or all combinations

Elementary Math Functions (Continued)

`real`	Real part of complex number
`rem`	Remainder after division
`round`	Round to nearest integer
`sec, sech`	Secant and hyperbolic secant
`sign`	Signum function
`sin, sinh`	Sine and hyperbolic sine
`sqrt`	Square root
`tan, tanh`	Tangent and hyperbolic tangent

Specialized Math Functions

This set of functions includes Bessel, elliptic, gamma, factorial, and others.

Specialized Math Functions

`airy`	Airy functions
`besselh`	Bessel functions of the third kind (Hankel functions)
`besseli, besselk`	Modified Bessel functions
`besselj, bessely`	Bessel functions
`beta, betainc, betaln`	beta, betainc, betaln
`ellipj`	Jacobi elliptic functions
`ellipke`	Complete elliptic integrals of the first and second kind
`erf, erfc, erfcx, erfinv`	Error functions
`expint`	Exponential integral
`factorial`	Factorial function
`gamma, gammainc, gammaln`	Gamma functions
`legendre`	Associated Legendre functions
`pow2`	Base 2 power and scale floating-point numbers
`rat, rats`	Rational fraction approximation

Coordinate System Conversion

Using these functions you can transform Cartesian coordinates to polar, cylindrical, or spherical, and vice versa.

Coordinate System Conversion

cart2pol	Transform Cartesian coordinates to polar or cylindrical
cart2sph	Transform Cartesian coordinates to spherical
pol2cart	Transform polar or cylindrical coordinates to Cartesian
sph2cart	Transform spherical coordinates to Cartesian

Matrix Functions - Numerical Linear Algebra

These functions let you perform matrix analysis including matrix determinant, rank, reduced row echelon form, eigenvalues, and inverses.

Matrix Analysis

cond	Condition number with respect to inversion
condeig	Condition number with respect to eigenvalues
det	Matrix determinant
norm	Vector and matrix norms
null	Null space of a matrix
orth	Range space of a matrix
rank	Rank of a matrix
rcond	Matrix reciprocal condition number estimate
rref, rrefmovie	Reduced row echelon form
subspace	Angle between two subspaces
trace	Sum of diagonal elements

Linear Equations

chol	Cholesky factorization
inv	Matrix inverse
lscov	Least squares solution in the presence of known covariance
lu	LU matrix factorization
lsqnonneg	Nonnegative least squares
pinv	Moore-Penrose pseudoinverse of a matrix
qr	Orthogonal-triangular decomposition

Eigenvalues and Singular Values

balance	Improve accuracy of computed eigenvalues
cdf2rdf	Convert complex diagonal form to real block diagonal form
eig	Eigenvalues and eigenvectors
gsvd	Generalized singular value decomposition
hess	Hessenberg form of a matrix
poly	Polynomial with specified roots
qz	QZ factorization for generalized eigenvalues
rsf2csf	Convert real Schur form to complex Schur form
schur	Schur decomposition
svd	Singular value decomposition

Matrix Functions

expm	Matrix exponential
funm	Evaluate functions of a matrix
logm	Matrix logarithm
sqrtm	Matrix square root

Low Level Functions

qrdelete	Delete column from QR factorization
qrinsert	Insert column in QR factorization

Data Analysis and Fourier Transform Functions

Using the data analysis functions, you can find permutations, prime numbers, mean, median, variance, correlation, and perform convolutions and other standard array manipulations. A set of vector functions lets you operate on vectors to find cross product, union, and other standard vector manipulations. The Fourier transform functions let you perform discrete Fourier transformations in one or more dimensions and their inverses.

Basic Operations

convhull	Convex hull
cumprod	Cumulative product
cumsum	Cumulative sum
cumtrapz	Cumulative trapezoidal numerical integration
delaunay	Delaunay triangulation
dsearch	Search for nearest point
factor	Prime factors
inpolygon	Detect points inside a polygonal region
max	Maximum elements of an array
mean	Average or mean value of arrays
median	Median value of arrays
min	Minimum elements of an array
perms	All possible permutations
polyarea	Area of polygon
primes	Generate list of prime numbers
prod	Product of array elements

Basic Operations (Continued)

sort	Sort elements in ascending order
sortrows	Sort rows in ascending order
std	Standard deviation
sum	Sum of array elements
trapz	Trapezoidal numerical integration
tsearch	Search for enclosing Delaunay triangle
var	Variance
voronoi	Voronoi diagram

Finite Differences

del2	Discrete Laplacian
diff	Differences and approximate derivatives
gradient	Numerical gradient

Correlation

corrcoef	Correlation coefficients
cov	Covariance matrix

Filtering and Convolution

conv	Convolution and polynomial multiplication
conv2	Two-dimensional convolution
deconv	Deconvolution and polynomial division
filter	Filter data with an infinite impulse response (IIR) or finite impulse response
filter2	Two-dimensional digital filtering

Fourier Transforms

abs	Absolute value and complex magnitude
angle	Phase angle
cplxpair	Sort complex numbers into complex conjugate pairs
fft	One-dimensional fast Fourier transform
fft2	Two-dimensional fast Fourier transform
fftshift	Shift DC component of fast Fourier transform to center of spectrum
ifft	Inverse one-dimensional fast Fourier transform
ifft2	Inverse two-dimensional fast Fourier transform
ifftn	Inverse multidimensional fast Fourier transform
ifftshift	Inverse FFT shift
nextpow2	Next power of two
unwrap	Correct phase angles

Vector Functions

cross	Vector cross product
intersect	Set intersection of two vectors
ismember	Detect members of a set
setdiff	Return the set difference of two vector
setxor	Set exclusive or of two vectors
union	Set union of two vectors
unique	Unique elements of a vector

Polynomial and Interpolation Functions

These functions let you operate on polynomials such as multiply, divide, find derivatives, and evaluate. The data interpolation functions let you perform interpolation in one, two, three, and higher dimensions.

Polynomials

conv	Convolution and polynomial multiplication
deconv	Deconvolution and polynomial division
poly	Polynomial with specified roots
polyder	Polynomial derivative
polyeig	Polynomial eigenvalue problem
polyfit	Polynomial curve fitting
polyval	Polynomial evaluation
polyvalm	Matrix polynomial evaluation
residue	Convert between partial fraction expansion and polynomial coefficients
roots	Polynomial roots

Data Interpolation

griddata	Data gridding
interp1	One-dimensional data interpolation (table lookup)
interp2	Two-dimensional data interpolation (table lookup)
interp3	Three-dimensional data interpolation (table lookup)
interpft	One-dimensional interpolation using the FFT method
interpn	Multidimensional data interpolation (table lookup)
meshgrid	Generate X and Y matrices for three-dimensional plots
ndgrid	Generate arrays for multidimensional functions and interpolation
spline	Cubic spline interpolation

Function Functions - Nonlinear Numerical Methods

Using these functions you can solve differential equations, perform numerical evaluation of integrals, and optimize functions.

Function Functions - Nonlinear Numerical Methods

dblquad	Numerical double integration
fminbnd	Minimize a function of one variable
fminsearch	Minimize a function of several variables
fzero	Zero of a function of one variable
ode45, ode23, ode113, ode15s, ode23s, ode23t, ode23tb	Solve differential equations
odefile	Define a differential equation problem for ODE solvers
odeget	Extract properties from options structure created with odeset
odeset	Create or alter options structure for input to ODE solvers
quad, quad8	Numerical evaluation of integrals
vectorize	Vectorize expression

Sparse Matrix Functions

These functions allow you to operate on a special type of matrix, sparse. Using these functions you can convert full to sparse, visualize, and operate on these matrices.

Elementary Sparse Matrices

spdiags	Extract and create sparse band and diagonal matrices
speye	Sparse identity matrix

Elementary Sparse Matrices (Continued)

sprand	Sparse uniformly distributed random matrix
sprandn	Sparse normally distributed random matrix
sprandsym	Sparse symmetric random matrix

Full to Sparse Conversion

find	Find indices and values of nonzero elements
full	Convert sparse matrix to full matrix
sparse	Create sparse matrix
spconvert	Import matrix from sparse matrix external format

Working with Nonzero Entries of Sparse Matrices

nnz	Number of nonzero matrix elements
nonzeros	Nonzero matrix elements
nzmax	Amount of storage allocated for nonzero matrix elements
spalloc	Allocate space for sparse matrix
spfun	Apply function to nonzero sparse matrix elements
spones	Replace nonzero sparse matrix elements with ones

Visualizing Sparse Matrices

spy	Visualize sparsity pattern

Reordering Algorithms

colmmd	Sparse column minimum degree permutation
colperm	Sparse column permutation based on nonzero count

Reordering Algorithms (Continued)

dmperm	Dulmage-Mendelsohn decomposition
randperm	Random permutation
symmmd	Sparse symmetric minimum degree ordering
symrcm	Sparse reverse Cuthill-McKee ordering

Norm, Condition Number, and Rank

condest	1-norm matrix condition number estimate
normest	2-norm estimate

Sparse Systems of Linear Equations

bicg	BiConjugate Gradients method
bicgstab	BiConjugate Gradients Stabilized method
cgs	Conjugate Gradients Squared method
cholinc	Sparse Incomplete Cholesky and Cholesky-Infinity factorizations
cholupdate	Rank 1 update to Cholesky factorization
gmres	Generalized Minimum Residual method (with restarts)
luinc	Incomplete LU matrix factorizations
pcg	Preconditioned Conjugate Gradients method
qmr	Quasi-Minimal Residual method
qr	Orthogonal-triangular decomposition
qrdelete	Delete column from QR factorization
qrinsert	Insert column in QR factorization
qrupdate	Rank 1 update to QR factorization

Sparse Eigenvalues and Singular Values

eigs	Find eigenvalues and eigenvectors
svds	Find singular values

Miscellaneous

spparms	Set parameters for sparse matrix routines

Sound Processing Functions

The sound processing functions let you convert signals, and read and write .au and .wav sound files.

General Sound Functions

lin2mu	Convert linear audio signal to mu-law
mu2lin	Convert mu-law audio signal to linear
sound	Convert vector into sound
soundsc	Scale data and play as sound

SPARCstation-Specific Sound Functions

auread	Read NeXT/SUN (.au) sound file
auwrite	Write NeXT/SUN (.au) sound file

.WAV Sound Functions

wavread	Read Microsoft WAVE (.wav) sound file
wavwrite	Write Microsoft WAVE (.wav) sound file

A-13

Character String Functions

This set of functions lets you manipulate strings such as comparison, concatenation, search, and conversion.

General

abs	Absolute value and complex magnitude
eval	Interpret strings containing MATLAB expressions
real	Real part of complex number
strings	MATLAB string handling

String Manipulation

deblank	Strip trailing blanks from the end of a string
findstr	Find one string within another
lower	Convert string to lower case
strcat	String concatenation
strcmp	Compare strings
strcmpi	Compare strings ignoring case
strjust	Justify a character array
strmatch	Find possible matches for a string
strncmp	Compare the first n characters of two strings
strrep	String search and replace
strtok	First token in string
strvcat	Vertical concatenation of strings
symvar	Determine symbolic variables in an expression
texlabel	Produce the TeX format from a character string
upper	Convert string to upper case

String to Number Conversion

char	Create character array (string)
int2str	Integer to string conversion
mat2str	Convert a matrix into a string
num2str	Number to string conversion
sprintf	Write formatted data to a string
sscanf	Read string under format control
str2double	Convert string to double-precision value
str2num	String to number conversion

Radix Conversion

bin2dec	Binary to decimal number conversion
dec2bin	Decimal to binary number conversion
dec2hex	Decimal to hexadecimal number conversion
hex2dec	IEEE hexadecimal to decimal number conversion
hex2num	Hexadecimal to double number conversion

Low-Level File I/O Functions

The low-level file I/O functions allow you to open and close files, read and write formatted and unformatted data, operate on files, and perform other specialized file I/O such as reading and writing images and spreadsheets.

File Opening and Closing

fclose	Close one or more open files
fopen	Open a file or obtain information about open files

Unformatted I/O

fread	Read binary data from file
fwrite	Write binary data to a file

Formatted I/O

fgetl	Return the next line of a file as a string without line terminator(s)
fgets	Return the next line of a file as a string with line terminator(s)
fprintf	Write formatted data to file
fscanf	Read formatted data from file

File Positioning

feof	Test for end-of-file
ferror	Query MATLAB about errors in file input or output
frewind	Rewind an open file
fseek	Set file position indicator
ftell	Get file position indicator

String Conversion

sprintf	Write formatted data to a string
sscanf	Read string under format control

Specialized File I/O

dlmread	Read an ASCII delimited file into a matrix
dlmwrite	Write a matrix to an ASCII delimited file
hdf	HDF interface
imfinfo	Return information about a graphics file
imread	Read image from graphics file
imwrite	Write an image to a graphics file
textread	Read formatted data from text file

Specialized File I/O (Continued)

wk1read	Read a Lotus123 WK1 spreadsheet file into a matrix
wk1write	Write a matrix to a Lotus123 WK1 spreadsheet file

Bitwise Functions

These functions let you operate at the bit level such as shifting and complementing.

Bitwise Functions

bitand	Bit-wise AND
bitcmp	Complement bits
bitor	Bit-wise OR
bitmax	Maximum floating-point integer
bitset	Set bit
bitshift	Bit-wise shift
bitget	Get bit
bitxor	Bit-wise XOR

Structure Functions

Structures are arrays whose elements can hold any MATLAB data type such as text, numeric arrays, or other structures. You access structure elements by name. Use the structure functions to create and operate on this array type.

Structure Functions

deal	Deal inputs to outputs
fieldnames	Field names of a structure
getfield	Get field of structure array
rmfield	Remove structure fields
setfield	Set field of structure array
struct	Create structure array
struct2cell	Structure to cell array conversion

Object Functions

Using the object functions you can create objects, detect objects of a given class, and return the class of an object.

Object Functions	
class	Create object or return class of object
isa	Detect an object of a given class

Cell Array Functions

Cell arrays are arrays comprised of cells, which can hold any MATLAB data type such as text, numeric arrays, or other cell arrays. Unlike structures, you access these cells by number. Use the cell array functions to create and operate on these arrays.

Cell Array Functions	
cell	Create cell array
cellfun	Apply a function to each element in a cell array
cellstr	Create cell array of strings from character array
cell2struct	Cell array to structure array conversion
celldisp	Display cell array contents
cellplot	Graphically display the structure of cell arrays
num2cell	Convert a numeric array into a cell array

Multidimensional Array Functions

These functions provide a mechanism for working with arrays of dimension greater than 2.

Multidimensional Array Functions	
cat	Concatenate arrays
flipdim	Flip array along a specified dimension
ind2sub	Subscripts from linear index
ipermute	Inverse permute the dimensions of a multidimensional array
ndgrid	Generate arrays for multidimensional functions and interpolation
ndims	Number of array dimensions
permute	Rearrange the dimensions of a multidimensional array
reshape	Reshape array
shiftdim	Shift dimensions
squeeze	Remove singleton dimensions
sub2ind	Single index from subscripts

Plotting and Data Visualization

This extensive set of functions gives you the ability to create basic graphs such as bar, pie, polar, and three-dimensional plots, and advanced graphs such as surface, mesh, contour, and volume visualization plots. In addition, you can use these functions to control lighting, color, view, and many other fine manipulations.

Basic Plots and Graphs	
bar	Vertical bar chart
barh	Horizontal bar chart
hist	Plot histograms
hold	Hold current graph
loglog	Plot using log-log scales
pie	Pie plot
plot	Plot vectors or matrices.
polar	Polar coordinate plot
semilogx	Semi-log scale plot

Basic Plots and Graphs (Continued)

semilogy	Semi-log scale plot
subplot	Create axes in tiled positions

Three-Dimensional Plotting

bar3	Vertical 3-D bar chart
bar3h	Horizontal 3-D bar chart
comet3	Three-dimensional comet plot
cylinder	Generate cylinder
fill3	Draw filled 3-D polygons in 3-space
plot3	Plot lines and points in 3-D space
quiver3	Three-dimensional quiver (or velocity) plot
slice	Volumetric slice plot
sphere	Generate sphere
stem3	Plot discrete surface data
waterfall	Waterfall plot

Plot Annotation and Grids

clabel	Add contour labels to a contour plot
datetick	Date formatted tick labels
grid	Grid lines for 2-D and 3-D plots
gtext	Place text on a 2-D graph using a mouse
legend	Graph legend for lines and patches
plotedit	Start plot edit mode to edit and annotate plots
plotyy	Plot graphs with Y tick labels on the left and right
title	Titles for 2-D and 3-D plots
xlabel	X-axis labels for 2-D and 3-D plots

Plot Annotation and Grids (Continued)

ylabel	Y-axis labels for 2-D and 3-D plots
zlabel	Z-axis labels for 3-D plots

Surface, Mesh, and Contour Plots

contour	Contour (level curves) plot
contourc	Contour computation
contourf	Filled contour plot
hidden	Mesh hidden line removal mode
meshc	Combination mesh/contourplot
mesh	3-D mesh with reference plane
peaks	A sample function of two variables
surf	3-D shaded surface graph
surface	Create surface low-level objects
surfc	Combination surf/contourplot
surfl	3-D shaded surface with lighting
trimesh	Triangular mesh plot
trisurf	Triangular surface plot

Volume Visualization

coneplot	Plot velocity vectors as cones in 3-D vector field
contourslice	Draw contours in volume slice plane
isocaps	Compute isosurface end-cap geometry
isonormals	Compute normals of isosurface vertices
isosurface	Extract isosurface data from volume data
reducepatch	Reduce the number of patch faces
reducevolume	Reduce number of elements in volume data set
shrinkfaces	Reduce the size of patch faces
smooth3	Smooth 3-D data

A-17

Volume Visualization (Continued)

stream2	Compute 2-D stream line data
stream3	Compute 3-D stream line data
streamline	Draw stream lines from 2- or 3-D vector data
surf2patch	Convert surface data to patch data
subvolume	Extract subset of volume data set

Domain Generation

griddata	Data gridding and surface fitting
meshgrid	Generation of X and Y arrays for 3-D plots

Specialized Plotting

area	Area plot
box	Axis box for 2-D and 3-D plots
comet	Comet plot
compass	Compass plot
convhull	Convex hull
delaunay	Delaunay triangulation
dsearch	Search Delaunay triangulation for nearest point
errorbar	Plot graph with error bars
ezcontour	Easy to use contour plotter
ezcontourf	Easy to use filled contour plotter
ezmesh	Easy to use 3-D mesh plotter
ezmeshc	Easy to use combination mesh/contour plotter
ezplot	Easy to use function plotter
ezplot3	Easy to use 3-D parametric curve plotter
ezpolar	Easy to use polar coordinate plotter
ezsurf	Easy to use 3-D colored surface plotter

Specialized Plotting (Continued)

ezsurfc	Easy to use combination surface/contour plotter
feather	Feather plot
fill	Draw filled 2-D polygons
fplot	Plot a function
inpolygon	True for points inside a polygonal region
pareto	Pareto char
pcolor	Pseudocolor (checkerboard) plot
pie3	Three-dimensional pie plot
plotmatrix	Scatter plot matrix
polyarea	Area of polygon
quiver	Quiver (or velocity) plot
ribbon	Ribbon plot
rose	Plot rose or angle histogram
scatter	Scatter plot
scatter3	Three-dimensional scatter plot
stairs	Stairstep graph
stem	Plot discrete sequence data
tsearch	Search for enclosing Delaunay triangle
voronoi	Voronoi diagram

View Control

camdolly	Move camera position and target
camlookat	View specific objects
camorbit	Orbit about camera target
campan	Rotate camera target about camera position
campos	Set or get camera position
camproj	Set or get projection type
camroll	Rotate camera about viewing axis
camtarget	Set or get camera target
camup	Set or get camera up-vector
camva	Set or get camera view angle

View Control (Continued)

camzoom	Zoom camera in or out
daspect	Set or get data aspect ratio
pbaspect	Set or get plot box aspect ratio
view	Three-dimensional graph viewpoint specification.
viewmtx	Generate view transformation matrices
xlim	Set or get the current x-axis limits
ylim	Set or get the current y-axis limits
zlim	Set or get the current z-axis limits

Lighting

camlight	Create or position a light
lightangle	Spherical position of a light
lighting	Lighting mode
material	Material reflectance mode

Color Operations

brighten	Brighten or darken color map
caxis	Pseudocolor axis scaling
colorbar	Display color bar (color scale)
colordef	Set up color defaults
colormap	Set the color look-up table
graymon	Graphics figure defaults set for grayscale monitor
hsv2rgb	Hue-saturation-value to red-green-blue conversion
rgb2hsv	RGB to HSV conversion
rgbplot	Plot color map
shading	Color shading mode
spinmap	Spin the colormap

Color Operations (Continued)

surfnorm	Three-dimensional surface normals
whitebg	Change axes background color for plots

Colormaps

autumn	Shades of red and yellow color map
bone	Gray-scale with a tinge of blue color map
contrast	Gray color map to enhance image contrast
cool	Shades of cyan and magenta color map
copper	Linear copper-tone color map
flag	Alternating red, white, blue, and black color map
gray	Linear gray-scale color map
hot	Black-red-yellow-white color map
hsv	Hue-saturation-value (HSV) color map
jet	Variant of HSV
lines	Line color colormap
prism	Colormap of prism colors
spring	Shades of magenta and yellow color map
summer	Shades of green and yellow colormap
winter	Shades of blue and green color map

Printing

orient	Hardcopy paper orientation
print	Print graph or save graph to file
printopt	Configure local printer defaults
saveas	Save figure to graphic file

Handle Graphics, General

copyobj	Make a copy of a graphics object and its children
findobj	Find objects with specified property values
gcbo	Return object whose callback is currently executing
gco	Return handle of current object
get	Get object properties
ishandle	True for graphics objects
rotate	Rotate objects about specified origin and direction
set	Set object properties

Handle Graphics, Object Creation

axes	Create axes object
figure	Create figure (graph) windows
image	Create image (2-D matrix)
light	Create light object (illuminates Patch and Surface)
line	Create line object (3-D polylines)
patch	Create patch object (polygons)
rectangle	Create rectangle object (2-D rectangle)
surface	Create surface (quadrilaterals)
text	Create text object (character strings)
uicontextmenu	Create context menu (pop-up associated with object)

Handle Graphics, Figure Windows

capture	Screen capture of the current figure
clc	Clear figure window
clf	Clear figure
close	Close specified window
gcf	Get current figure handle

Handle Graphics, Figure Windows (Continued)

newplot	Graphics M-file preamble for NextPlot property
refresh	Refresh figure
saveas	Save figure or model to desired output format

Handle Graphics, Axes

axis	Plot axis scaling and appearance
cla	Clear axes
gca	Get current axes handle

Object Manipulation

reset	Reset axis or figure
rotate3d	Interactively rotate the view of a 3-D plot
selectmoveresize	Interactively select, move, or resize objects

Interactive User Input

ginput	Graphical input from a mouse or cursor
zoom	Zoom in and out on a 2-D plot

Region of Interest

dragrect	Drag XOR rectangles with mouse
drawnow	Complete any pending drawing
rbbox	Rubberband box

Graphical User Interface Creation

The graphical user interface functions let you build your own interfaces for your applications.

Dialog Boxes

dialog	Create a dialog box
errordlg	Create error dialog box

Dialog Boxes (Continued)

helpdlg	Display help dialog box
inputdlg	Create input dialog box
listdlg	Create list selection dialog box
msgbox	Create message dialog box
pagedlg	Display page layout dialog box
printdlg	Display print dialog box
questdlg	Create question dialog box
uigetfile	Display dialog box to retrieve name of file for reading
uiputfile	Display dialog box to retrieve name of file for writing
uisetcolor	Interactively set a ColorSpec using a dialog box
uisetfont	Interactively set a font using a dialog box
warndlg	Create warning dialog box

User Interface Objects

menu	Generate a menu of choices for user input
uicontextmenu	Create context menu
uicontrol	Create user interface control
uimenu	Create user interface menu

Other Functions

dragrect	Drag rectangles with mouse
gcbo	Return handle of object whose callback is executing
rbbox	Create rubberband box for area selection
selectmoveresize	Select, move, resize, or copy axes and uicontrol graphics objects
textwrap	Return wrapped string matrix for given uicontrol
uiresume	Used with uiwait, controls program execution

Other Functions (Continued)

uiwait	Used with uiresume, controls program execution
waitbar	Display wait bar
waitforbuttonpress	Wait for key/buttonpress over figure

Symbolic Math Toolbox Quick Reference

Introduction

This appendix lists the Symbolic Math Toolbox functions that are available in the Student Version of MATLAB & Simulink. For complete information about any of these functions, use the Help Desk and either:

- Select the function from the **Symbolic Math Toolbox Functions**, or
- Select **Online Manuals** and view the *Symbolic Math Toolbox User's Guide*.

Note All of the functions listed in Symbolic Math Toolbox Functions are available in the Student Version of MATLAB & Simulink *except* `maple`, `mapleinit`, `mfun`, `mfunlist`, and `mhelp`.

Arithmetic Operations

+	Addition
-	Subtraction
*	Multiplication
.*	Array multiplication
/	Right division
./	Array right division
\	Left division
.\	Array left division
^	Matrix or scalar raised to a power
.^	Array raised to a power
'	Complex conjugate transpose
.'	Real transpose

Basic Operations

ccode	C code representation of a symbolic expression
conj	Complex conjugate
findsym	Determine symbolic variables
fortran	Fortran representation of a symbolic expression
imag	Imaginary part of a complex number
latex	LaTeX representation of a symbolic expression
pretty	Pretty print a symbolic expression
real	Real part of an imaginary number
sym	Create symbolic object
syms	Shortcut for creating multiple symbolic objects

Calculus

diff	Differentiate
int	Integrate
jacobian	Jacobian matrix
limit	Limit of an expression

Calculus (Continued)

symsum	Summation of series
taylor	Taylor series expansion

Conversions

char	Convert sym object to string
double	Convert symbolic matrix to double
poly2sym	Function calculator
sym2poly	Symbolic polynomial to coefficient vector

Integral Transforms

fourier	Fourier transform
ifourier	Inverse Fourier transform
ilaplace	Inverse Laplace transform
iztrans	Inverse z-transform
laplace	Laplace transform
ztrans	z-transform

Linear Algebra

colspace	Basis for column space
det	Determinant
diag	Create or extract diagonals
eig	Eigenvalues and eigenvectors
expm	Matrix exponential
inv	Matrix inverse
jordan	Jordan canonical form
null	Basis for null space
poly	Characteristic polynomial
rank	Matrix rank
rref	Reduced row echelon form
svd	Singular value decomposition
tril	Lower triangle
triu	Upper triangle

Pedagogical and Graphical Applications

ezplot	Easy-to-use function plotter
funtool	Function calculator
rsums	Riemann sums

Simplification

collect	Collect common terms
expand	Expand polynomials and elementary functions
factor	Factor
horner	Nested polynomial representation
numden	Numerator and denominator
simple	Search for shortest form
simplify	Simplification
subexpr	Rewrite in terms of subexpressions

Solution of Equations

compose	Functional composition
dsolve	Solution of differential equations
finverse	Functional inverse
solve	Solution of algebraic equations

Variable Precision Arithmetic

digits	Set variable precision accuracy
vpa	Variable precision arithmetic

Index

Symbols

A

B

C